Also by Davis MacDonald

The Hill (set in Palos Verdes), Book 1 in the Judge Series.

The Island (set in Avalon, Catalina Island), Book 2 in the Judge Series.

Silicon Beach (set in Santa Monica and the LA West Side), Book 3 in the Judge Series.

The Bay (set in Newport Beach), Book 4 in the Judge Series.

Cabo (set in Cabo San Lucas), Book 5 in the Judge Series.

The Strand (set in the Los Angeles South Bay), Book 6 in the Judge Series (This Book).

The Lake (set in Lake Arrowhead), Book 7 in the Judge Series (due out in November of 2019).

I hope you enjoy **THE STRAND**, and if you do, please drop a brief positive review on Amazon for me. Your review will be greatly appreciated.

Watch for announcements for future books at:
http://davismacdonald-author.com/

Davis MacDonald

THE
STRAND

**A MYSTERY NOVEL
SET IN
SOUTHERN CALIFORNIA**

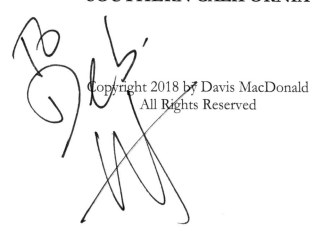

Copyright 2018 by Davis MacDonald
All Rights Reserved

"'tis much more Prudence to acquit two Persons, tho' actually guilty, than to pass Sentence of Condemnation on one that is virtuous and innocent."
Voltaire

"Ethics is knowing the difference between what you have a right to do and what is right to do."
Justice Potter Stewart

"The dog barks, but the Caravan moves on!"
Arab Proverb

A Note From the Author

This story, and its characters, events, locations and scenes, although completely fictional, are inspired in part by the facts of several criminal cases.

CHAPTER 1

The Judge pulled into a parking space facing the Ocean Hill Pier to enjoy his Starbucks. And to watch the huge waves pounding the beach and the pier. A storm in Mexico had ignited the surf up and down the west-facing beaches, making for a stunning display of foaming white surf and churning green water, some waves reaching ten feet.

The pier was taking a beating. He wished he'd time to walk out onto the concrete structure. He imagined his hair flying in the salty spray, the smell of the waves filling his nostrils, feet planted against the raging wind, wrapped in the old raincoat he kept in the trunk. Like a swashbuckling Scottish sea captain of old, feet planted on the bit of flotsam that was his ship.

But it was a fantasy. There wasn't time. He took a long slug of his Starbucks, feeling the caffeine hit his bloodstream like a kick in the pants. Waking him up. He wiped latte foam from his upper lip.

He was on route from home in Palos Verdes to his office in Venice. But he'd stopped in the City of Ocean Hill, a small but affluent community tucked above Hermosa Beach to the south, and LAX to the north, fronting some of the best beach in California. He had to go into the office today. One more case to tidy up. But it seemed like it was always one more. For thirty years now, always just one more case. Time went

1

by, you grew older, a little less hair to comb, a little harder to read the newspaper, a little shorter on exercise, a little more weight to haul around, a little tougher to see the scale under your tummy. Days, weeks, months all flew by quicker now, the 'To Do' list got longer, and you weren't as quick checking things off. Perhaps because you didn't have all the answers now, answers that came so easily and with such conviction in your youth. But then maybe you were right more often now, fewer answers but better ones he supposed, although sometimes he wasn't so sure.

And he was now responsible for his family. Katy, twenty years his junior. And their joint creation, Ralphie, only just five, a young man wondering why his dad wasn't any good at baseball or basketball. Why his dad was so… old.

This domestic gig was still relatively new for him. Just five years. He'd mostly been a solitary creature, by happenstance, by nature, living on this Southern California plain of crowded humanity: social animals with herd instincts, ready to praise or damn whomever the combined collective deemed worthy or unworthy, whomever ignited and swayed the passions of the day, ready to believe the best or the worst about anybody or anything that captured the popular imagination.

He'd been a judge. Now he was a practicing lawyer. Each client was different but he'd often pressed against a tide of public opinion and condemnation, representing underdogs, asserting the individual rights of his clients and challenging uninformed condemnation from a society more interested in exposé and drama then verifiable facts. It was his calling. But it was hard work, stressful, and he was getting tired.

Sitting in that parking lot briefly, watching the waves crash up under the pier, he had no premonition of the immense wave of public opinion about to form, about to rise into a towering swell behind him, only to come toppling down, crashing over him, over his bride Katy and even over little Ralphie, churning them in a cauldron of confusion, social stigma, hate and even violence.

He pulled back out of the beach parking lot, up Ocean Hill Boulevard, then left on Highland, parallel to the ocean, threading his way through traffic, heading for North Ocean Hill and Dockweiler Beach beyond, his secret route into Venice. He stopped as the light went red at Highland and 40th, glancing down 40th Street at the water and the roiled surf. It was spectacular.

A small blond man was making his way up the street from the direction of the beach, head down, trudging really, although he seemed young. He was partially pulled uphill by a scruffy looking dog on a leash, a mutt, part terrier, part poodle perhaps, with greying hair and old eyes.

As the Judge watched, a motorcycle darted out from a side alley below, swerved uphill, rumbled past the man full tilt, and collided into the back of the dog, sending the animal sprawling, yanking the leash from the man's hand. The biker careened around in a U-turn, tearing back down the street past the pile of rumpled fur and a now screaming young man, and then cut down the alley-like cross-street below, disappearing in a cloud of smoke and fumes with a roar that echoed down the narrow canyon between the houses.

The blond man screamed, "No... No...," rushed the five steps to stoop over the animal, then sank to his knees beside it. He lifted the broken dog into his arms, fluids draining onto the pavement as the creature went into its final throws. Tears streamed down the man's face as he cradled the animal. It gave one last spontaneous jerk, then went still.

The Judge's light had gone green and the car behind him honked threateningly. He moved forward, the tableau down the side street disappearing behind the facade of the gym occupying the corner, and then the follow-on mixed-use clutter that was Highland in North Ocean Hill.

Jesus, mused the Judge. *A hit and run on a dog. What the fuck?* Life seemed more uncertain every day in this dusty bowl plateau people called L.A.

People liked to pretend everything was orderly, in its place. We're born, go to school, party at college, settle with a mate and steady job, buy a house or condo, raise kids, send them off to college, settle into the haze of senior status, awakened now and then by visits from lusty grandchildren, then fade off into old age. Or so it was supposed.

But how many ways did the plan go wrong? Twelve percent of people would die in an accident, sixteen percent would die of a heart attack, five percent were out of a job because of the Great Recession and perhaps on the way to being homeless. Fifty percent would have marriages ending in divorce. Others would discover their retirement plans under-funded, barely scraping by in their 'Golden Years'. The American

4

Dream was only that, a dream. Reality was that poor guy back there, holding his crushed animal.

The Judge turned left at the next street, left again at the alley and left onto 40th where the animal had been run down, thinking he might help. But two pedestrians were already to either side of the kneeling man, trying to calm him. He was still sobbing, refusing to let go of the ball of grey fur in his arms.

The Judge pedaled the gas and moved on, back up to the signal, now green, taking the corner and resuming his route toward Dockweiler, Venice and his office, trying to let go of the image of the man and his dog.

CHAPTER 2

The Judge tried not to grind his teeth as he waited to drop Ralphie off at pre-school, preferring to pulverize the brake-pedal with his foot, grinding back and forth across its surface, occasionally releasing it to move forward an inch or three before pushing hard again. The line of cars slowly crawled forward now and then with all the speed of a conga line of geriatric snails. The exhaust from three idling SUVs and seven large sedans perfumed the air, reaching through his car's venting system, leaving the inside arid and pungent.

Little Ralphie, snared in his raised car seat behind the Judge and pitched so he could see out the front window and both sides like some Oriental Potentate, didn't mind. He grasped a brown paper bag in one hand with a death grip, his snack bag, and was all big eyes on a tiny swiveling head, watching the people and the brightly colored cars and SUVs finally reaching the head of the line and dumping their small passengers.

This was a new system. And a foul system it was. Instead of allowing parents to walk their kids into their designated classrooms, the Pre-School had put a stop to the aimless and generally uncontrollable swarms of adults invading their sacred grounds twice a day. This new system had teachers and assorted staff meeting the little buggers at the designated car drop-off point, helping them out of their car-seats, and escorting them hand-and-hand into the school.

The plan sounded fine in theory, but quickly wrecked itself on the shoals of reality. Most of the drop-off parents were moms and most of the pre-school staff were female. The resulting interaction was a golden opportunity to use female words, chit-chatting with each other at length, leaving a line of stranded cars and females behind, waiting their turn to use their female words.

This was the last time Katy would suck him into drop-off duty, he swore to God.

"Daddy."

"Yes, Ralphie"

"I like Mr. Harry."

"That's nice."

"He can fly."

"Oh. Well that's pretty cool. Have you seen him do it?"

"No. But he told us."

"I see."

"We're going to learn to play Naked Movie Star."

"What?" The Judge swung his head around shark-like in his seat to look at his small son, eye to eye, suddenly alert, focused.

"Yep. *What you say, is what you are, You're a naked movie star.* Ralphie giggled. "Maybe you'll play with me."

"Yes, Ralphie. You'll have to show me how you play when I get home tonight. Your mother can play too. I'm sure she'll want to hear all about it."

Ralphie nodded his satisfaction.

The Judge shook his head. He never knew what Ralphie would come up with next. It was all very… disconcerting.

The Strand Pre-School, or just The Strand, as it was called by locals, had been a South Bay institution for over forty years. Named after the famous Strand bike/walking path that extended from South Redondo, north through Hermosa Beach, through Ocean Hill, and all the way to Playa del Rey, the school was one of the oldest and most prestigious preschools servicing the small cities that checkered the beach from Palos Verdes to Playa Del Rey.

Many sons and daughters of the beach cities' elite had attended the school. Old Mary Wilson had founded the school years before but was now retired. The Strand was run by Mary's daughter, Laura Wilson, and Mary's son, Harry Wilson. The son did the back-office work and managed several classes. Demand was so great it was difficult to get a child into The Strand. There was a long waiting list. But the list could be circumvented if you knew the right people.

And the Judge had known old lady Mary Wilson since his youth when his mother and Mary had been bridge-partners. They used to say you could land his mother on the moon, and inside a week she'd have a bridge group organized and going. And he knew the daughter and current head master, Laura Wilson, too; perhaps better than he should. He smirked at that thought. He'd made a discreet call, and magically Ralphie had gotten an invitation to attend three days later, starting mid-term, making the Judge a hero to Katy, the Judge's bride. Ralphie seemed to enjoy himself at The Strand. He was excited to be hauled over each morning from Palos Verdes to attend.

The Judge finally pulled his car up to the assigned speed bump, and unlocked the passenger doors. The right-rear door was opened by Miss Johnsen, a lady of long years and loving girth who'd had no kids of her own, but seemed to love all kids, everywhere, all at once. With difficulty, she squeezed her bulk across the rear seat and child seat to reach the belt releases for Ralphie, and he immediately propelled himself out like a torpedo, using the old rubber man, sliding to the floor beneath her and squeezing out onto the pavement before she could regain her balance. Ralphie hopped up and down on one leg and then on the other, testing to be sure they still worked, the Judge supposed. They seemed okay.

"Hello and goodbye, Miss Johnsen," said the Judge, beating her to the draw, precluding some lame comment about the weather or other extraneous gossip, giving her his best boyish smile.

"Goodbye, Judge. Here, grab my hand, Ralphie."

It was then the front passenger-side door flew open and a tall redhead, in a pleated skirt and a white silk top cut low across the chest, squatted down beside the car so she could see the Judge, beautiful blue eyes pinning his. It was Laura Wilson, the daughter of the school founder and now Head Mistress, mid-thirties, recently divorced, and on the prowl, or so the Judge had heard. He liked to keep track of old flames for memories' sake.

Ten years earlier, when the Judge had been in his early forties and Laura had been in her twenties, they'd had a torrid affair. She's been a fire-fighter then, a big broad-shouldered girl with large breasts and strong thighs, standing five foot eleven, all muscle, competitive and hot. Laura had proven to be an almost insatiable lover. Their flame had been fueled by champagne, the special attraction between a younger woman and an older man, and a scent of musk that lingered even now as she leaned into his car, some pheromone link between them that descended from the beginnings of the race.

It hadn't lasted long, mostly because they'd worn each other out, both high strung workaholics, passionate in bed and passionate in careers, all great excitement, but never downtime, never able to just relax together.

And their politics hadn't helped. Laura had told the Judge once he was so conservative, he was to the right of Attila the Hun. The fact was that Laura was way liberal, even for a socialist. They'd discussed social and political issues of the day, often ending in shouting matches that left bruised feelings and dry interludes in their relationship, such as it was. But God she'd been wild in bed.

A year after their brief connection ended, she'd bailed from the Fire Department, disgusted with the rampant macho discrimination there, and come back to work in the family business, The Strand Pre-School, taking over as principal when her mother retired three years before.

The Judge ran his eyes over her as she bent down and forward to whisper something to him. Her soft white blouse curved around bountiful breasts, disclosing more than was legal as she bent low, framed by broad shoulders and the soft curls of blazing red hair, a light swath of freckles across her nose and cheeks contrasting with the baby blue eyes regarding him intently. Her beige skirt was stretched tight over a flat stomach and powerful thighs, supporting the still muscular legs of a one-time fire-fighter.

She looked great, a little older, a little wiser, but she'd maintained her athlete's body, buff and fit. And her blue eyes danced at the Judge for a second as she gazed at him. He had a fondness for her that transcended the years, as one has for old lovers.

But this morning there was heavy stress etched across her face, emphasizing the beginnings of lines that come in the thirties. She looked around conspiratorially to make sure no one could overhear, then whispered, tension cracking her voice.

"Judge. I've got a big problem."

"What?"

"Someone's dead."

"What?"

"Someone's dead."

"Who?"

"Jeffrey Simpson, our maintenance man."

"Where?"

"In the maintenance room. I don't know what to do. I need your help."

The Judge sighed. Why was it always him?

"Okay. Have you called Nine-One-One?"

"It's too late for that."

"Are you sure?'

"Yes. Jeffrey's very dead. I can't have my children upset by a fire engine, rescue truck and ambulance roaring onto the school grounds, sirens blaring all to hell and gone. You know how they are."

The Judge didn't, but Laura would.

It would be the parents upset, thought the Judge cynically. The parents who paid the freight. He was certain the children would love to see a fire engine roll in.

"Give me a minute, I'll park."

She slammed his passenger door with a vengeance, taking her anxiety out on his car, then stood back from the line, arms folded defensively across her chest, chewing her lower lip.

He parked and walked back to the drop-off bump, past the congregating cars. He'd forgotten how big Laura was, tall and powerful. She leaned against the wall of the school like some giant cat, her body exuding sexuality. No wonder he'd been so attracted. He still was. When she pushed off the wall and stood straight, he was a little taller than her, but not much.

The Judge was tall, broad shouldered and big boned, with just a bit of a paunch around the middle. Big hands, big feet, big ears and a big nose set in the middle of his squared ruddy Welsh face. With his short-cut dark hair, faded blue Polo shirt and ragtag jeans, he might have been a roustabout, or a laborer. Except for the eyes, large piercing blue eyes restlessly sweeping the people and space around him, missing nothing. Except that he was a lawyer. Except that he thought like a judge.

He rarely used his given name anymore. When he had ascended to the bench years back, people called him just Judge. Even old friends he'd known for years affectionately adopted the nickname. Back then it had seemed to fit. And somehow it had stuck even though he was no longer a judge. Now just another L.A. lawyer, scrambling for business in an over-crowded profession in an over-crowded city.

"Okay, Laura," he said, "let's have a look."

She smiled when he used her given name, a twinkle appearing briefly in the blue eyes, the sins of the past nudging her memory for an instant, before reality returned.

She marched him though the line of disembarking toddlers, each with a keeper's large hand wrapped around one small paw and a snack bag or lunch box clutched in the other. They walked through the iron gate entrance and across a red-tiled inner patio into the Spanish-style school building dating from the Thirties. They moved down a long hall to the left that ended at a door. She produced a key and unlocked the door, which swung out into the hall. She opened it just enough for the Judge to squeeze through, which turned out to be considerable given his paunch. She released the door, slipping through into the little room just before it closed silently on well-oiled springs, a lock sliding into place again.

The Judge felt closed in, as though in a tomb. It was a long, narrow, shrouded room. Gauzy light peered in from a high window set in the far wall. The room had the faint flavor of old floor polish, paint, turpentine... and something else. The something else wasn't good. It made the hair stand on the back of the Judge's neck.

A wooden workbench ran down the right side, anchored by a vise at the front corner, and a table saw of ancient vintage at the other. Under it was shoved a dog's bed, and an empty water bowl. Boxes of nails, screws, electrical parts, and hand tools were scattered across its surface, along with two small cans of touch-up paint and a box of rags. More tools hung on pock-marked plyboard nailed on the wall above the workbench, each tool bracketed in a cutout drawing of itself. A beat-up beach cruiser bicycle with faded aqua paint and rusty handlebars leaned against the workbench at its far end.

Beyond the workbench, set against the wall, and running to the window, was a small single bed with a cheerful looking comforter, silk, in a pattern of purple violets and green vines on a white background, complemented by matching shams and bed ruffle. But for the daybed, the overall impression of the maintenance room was of a man-cave, without the de rigueur refrigerator and beer.

"Does someone sleep here?" asked the Judge.

"Yes, Jeffrey, our maintenance man does, or did. His job was to be on call. We don't need him all the time. He's been here about six months. We've been cutting expenses to survive, and I'd gave him notice of termination a week ago." His last day was supposed to be tomorrow."

Four feet out from the wall on the left side of the room was a floor-to-ceiling rack of metal shelving running the length of the room, extending almost to the window wall, placed so one could walk behind it and access its contents from the other side by sliding past its end under the gauzy window. The shelving was laden with old file boxes, perhaps school records, and larger cardboard boxes, some lidless with old light fixtures, plumbing parts, and other odds and ends from the beginning of time.

Opposite the bed was a small TV, tucked into a space on the shelving, its empty screen dully reflecting the muted light from the window. The orange and turquoise cases for several newer electrical tools were neatly stowed next to the TV, filling the shelves.

"This way, Judge," said Laura, standing on her toes to reach a string to an overhead light, giving it an anxious jerk to shed neon white on the floor and walls around them.

She led him down to the window wall and then stopped, turning her head away, pointing the Judge around the corner of the shelving. The Judge stepped around her into the narrow space between wall and shelving rack. The light penetrated little into the gloom here. He immediately ran into someone's shoe floating three feet off the floor. He gasped as he jumped back.

CHAPTER 3

The Judge looked up. A large steel pipe was anchored cross the ceiling beams. A body dangled from it, swinging partly around from his collision with the shoe, displaying dusty jeans and a khaki shirt with large pockets, the beltless pants starting to slip down over narrow hips. The missing belt was wrapped around the pipe, the beam above, and around the body's neck. It was a man... or had been.

The man's head slumped to the left, his face fixed in contorted agony as he'd asphyxiated. He looked to have been late twenties or early thirties, lean and short, perhaps five foot four, with long blond hair and a surfer's good looks. There was something familiar about his face, but the Judge couldn't place him.

The man's face was just now turning mottled and splotched with purple. His pants were wet with released fluids, and a small pool had formed on the concrete floor under his hanging feet and run downhill to the wall parallel to the shelving, seeping under it. The fluids scented the air, not pleasantly. It was what the Judge first smelt when he'd stepped into the room.

A wooden stool turned on its side lay on the floor behind the body where it'd apparently been kicked, mostly white, some pink, green and brown varnish showing through old scars in the wood. Beside it was one shoe, kicked off in the man's instinctual and frantic struggles as he hung above, out of air, twisting and squirming in a last desperate attempt for life.

"This is Jeffrey?"

"Yes," said Laura Wilson in a small voice, her face still turned away. He could feel her intake of breath, the effort she was making to retain control. The Judge reached over and took hold of one of Jeffrey's hands. It was ice cold. Jeffrey had hung there a while in this dark cool place, much like a slab of beef in a cooler.

Laura suddenly started to dry-retch behind him. He turned and moved back to her, throwing his arms out, catching her across her breasts from behind as she started to fall, leaning her against him under the window, holding her tight as she fought to recover. A brief remembrance of earlier days holding her like this flashed through his mind. And other memories, triggered by her smell and the softness of her bosom. It was difficult to push them aside. Her scent and nearness briefly masked the presence of death.

He put those thoughts into a box somewhere in his head and closed its lid. Quickly... perhaps too quickly.

Once her breathing came back to somewhere close to regular, he unclasped his hands and led her past the long workbench to the door. Taking her key from her hand, he unlocked the door and started to swing it quickly into the hall, hoping to be free of the smell. But it stopped with a thud a third of the way open, producing a yelp on the other side. Someone had been in the hall next to the door. Listening perhaps?

Gingerly moving the door more open as the person moved away, the Judge opened it wide to disclose a young man standing there, late twenties, tall, with fluffy blond hair. Dark brown eyes flashed anger as the man rubbed one of his elbows with his hand. He wore black designer jeans and a black polo T-shirt, the kind the Judge detested because there was no shirt pocket. Tall, perhaps six-foot-one, he had a long narrow head, matching an aquiline nose, and bushy eyebrows of dark brown belying the blond color of his curls. *Bleach-Boy grows up*, mused the Judge.

"Harry, you're here," Laura said, stumbling around the Judge to grab Harry for support. "We've got a big problem."

"What? What's going on, Sis? Who's he?" He stabbed an aggressive finger at the Judge.

"Jeffrey Simpson is dead."

"No. How?"

"Hung himself."

"Jesus Christ. We don't need this, Sis. Not now. What're we going to do?"

"I don't know, Harry."

"Jesus, Laura, you said you were going to fire him. Did you? Did he know? Did you tell him he was out? Is that why?"

"I don't know, Harry. I told him last week. His last day was to be tomorrow."

"Shit. And who's this?" Harry turned to give the Judge another unfriendly glare.

"This is the Judge. An old friend. He's helping me because you weren't in yet. Judge, this is Harry, my kid brother."

The young man nodded, anger slowly replaced by something else in his eyes. Whatever it was, it wasn't friendly.

"Oh, sweet Jesus, Judge, what are we going to do?" Laura whispered, repeating Harry's question.

"We need to call Nine-One-One," said the Judge.

"But the school, the kids?"

"I don't suppose you can just send them home?" asked the Judge.

"No. Lots of working parents. For a lot of families, there's likely no one at home. No one available to pick up the kid at this hour."

"Let's put everyone in your activity room," said the Judge. "Close the doors. Your staff can entertain them there. Let the police do their work without an audience."

"Yes. That's exactly what we should do. You're right Judge. Can you call Nine-One-One and talk to the police? Harry and I will organize the kids and the staff into the activity room."

"They'll want to talk to you too, Laura. And no doubt Harry."

"Yes, I guess they will."

"How did you find the body?"

"I didn't see him come in this morning. But we've a hall light out. It needs the big ladder to replace the bulb. I couldn't find him, so I went looking. I finally tried the maintenance room. Oh God. I can't believe this is happening."

"You checked inside, even though the door was locked?"

"Yes. It's always kept locked, even when someone is in there, so the children can't get in."

"You found him like that?"

19

"Yes. I touched him. He was very… cold. So, I knew."

"Why'd you go all the way to the back of the room and look behind the racks?"

"I don't know. There was something odd, wrong. Perhaps the odor."

"And the door to the room was definitely locked?"

"Yes. I unlocked it when I came in. When it closes it locks on both sides. I used my key again to let myself out. I didn't want any of the kids to see."

"Is there another way in?"

"No."

"Did he seem depressed, or despondent, when you saw him last?"

"No. Not that I noticed."

"When did you see him last?"

"Oh God. Last night."

"Not this morning?"

"No."

"Hey," inserted Harry. "You're not the police. This sounds like an interrogation. You don't have to answer his questions, Laura."

The Judge held up his hands. "Just trying to figure out what happened."

"Let's have the police do that. What's your relationship with my sister now, anyhow, Mr. Judge? You used to be her boyfriend, didn't you?"

Laura sighed. "Harry, don't. Don't make a scene. The Judge is just a friend now. We haven't been an item in years. But he was dropping off his son today, and I saw him. I knew I could count on him to help."

"Why don't you two go organize your staff?" the Judge offered. "We can talk later. Right now, I'd better call the police."

"Can you give me a five-minute head start, Judge?" asked Laura.

"I suppose. Jeff the maintenance man isn't going anywhere on his own."

Laura pressed the key into the Judge's hand, then she and Harry headed down the hall, Laura still looking wobbly.

The Judge moved to the maintenance room and used the key to get back in. He walked the length of the workbench and sat down for a minute on the daybed. On the shelf facing him was the old TV. He leaned over, picked up its controller off the top of the set, and turned it on.

A soap opera flashed on, showing a heavily made-up well-endowed woman, verbally thrashing a small balding man with a clipped mustache in Spanish, while Mexican mariachis sang somewhere in the background. He switched the TV off.

The odor in the room was worse, now. He stood up and moved around the corner of the shelving. The body had stopped rotating and hung still, very still. Looking less like a man by the minute, changing as the temperature of the day increased.

Looking at the face, distorted though it was, the Judge again had the sense he'd seen the man before. He couldn't put his finger on where.

On the shelf beside the body were pruning shears. The shears rested atop a disreputable looking pair of green rubber gloves. He leaned over to look without touching. There were tiny strands of twine on

21

one blade. Looking closely at the floor, there was fluff of similar color. Had twine been used here? Perhaps to tie Jeffrey's hands while he was hung?

The Judge reached up and examined one of Jeffrey's wrists, then the other. No marks to indicate the wrists had been tied as far as he could tell, but the light was dim.

The Judge looked on the floor and under the racks; there was no written note. No message in the dust of the floor that said, '*This is suicide, I'm taking my own life.*' But the position of the body and the kicked-over stool suggested Jeffrey had snuffed himself.

The Judge edged around the body and along the back side of the shelf running the length of the room, using the light on his cell phone for guidance. It was tight, perhaps three feet between the shelf and the wood paneled wall. The floor was clean, no note, no message, no footprint. As though recently swept, except for two pieces of clear folded plastic tossed in the far corner and the fluff.

The Judge turned and sent his light back along his path, then edged his way back. As he approached the hanging carcass, he noted his footprint in the pool of material beneath. The police wouldn't be happy.

The Judge suddenly felt closed in, claustrophobic. He couldn't breathe. The smell had become overpowering. He edged around the body again, holding his breath now, trying to rob his brain of the awful smell, making a bolt for the corner of the rack, slamming around it, moving past the daybed, past the workbench, fumbling with the damn key, finally opening the door into the hall, sliding through into the fresh air beyond.

He braced himself against hallway wall, gasping as the door noiselessly swung closed behind him, locking itself again. He hung there for a minute, pinned to the wall, gulping air. Then he took out his cell, fumbled with Google until he found the direct number of the Ocean Hill Police Department, and dialed.

He reported finding the body at The Strand Pre-School, and requested the police not use sirens when they and the rescue truck came. Then he wandered outside, across the entry patio to the front of the school, out to the street and the speed bump where his day had suddenly gone wrong. He squatted down on the curb there, waiting for someone to come.

The long line of cars was gone. All the kids had been dropped off and the parents had roared away in their fancy rides. He wondered what he'd got himself into. He thought too about all the gas he burned and the fumes he'd inhaled, sitting in the stupid drop-off line. Tomorrow it'd damn well be his wife's ass and gas, not his.

CHAPTER 4

The fire rescue truck arrived first, then a fire engine, an ambulance, and not one but two black-and-whites. They were all blaring their sirens. *Boys would be boys*, mused the Judge.

It was a little odd there were two police cars rather than one. The Judge brushed the thought aside. He had to explain the situation first to the rescue truck crew, then again to the ambulance team, again to the fire engine crew, and finally to the police officers. They each took a trot into the school and down the hall to the maintenance room with him to have a peek, taking turns like relay teams in a cross-country walk-a-thon, but in some predetermined pecking order only they knew.

Ten minutes later a plainclothesman showed up in an unmarked car, solo, and took his own look-see, then returned. He was a big man, big feet, big hands, and a ponderous belly, covered over by a not so well tailored suit. He walked like his feet hurt and wore a countenance to match. He marched over to the Judge with a bland smile and introduced himself as Detective Hardy. The Judge wondered with a little envy how many daily donuts it required to maintain a figure like his. It was an idle thought. Katy, his bride, didn't let him have donuts anymore, not even the occasional Krispy Kreme, his favorite.

Hardy told the Judge they were sealing off the entire end of the hallway in front of the maintenance room and there'd be a full investigation. He brought out his flip-top notebook and eyed the Judge, suspicion etched into the folds of his chubby face.

"So, you just walked into the maintenance room and found the body of Mr. Jeff Simpson?"

"Yes. I mean Laura did. Then she brought me back to show me."

"That's Laura Wilson, the high muckety-muck owner?"

"Yes."

"Is there any other way in?"

"Not that I know of."

"I've heard there are underground tunnels under the school leading all over. Is that right?"

"I wouldn't know. I don't work here."

"So, what are you doing here? You don't look like a pre-school kid. You say you don't work here. Exactly why are you here this morning with all these young children running around?"

"One of the young people is my son. I'm a dad."

"Do dads have a habit of hanging around after school starts, either in the maintenance room or on the grounds?"

"Laura found the body, like I said."

"And?"

"She asked me to come have a look and help her."

"So, it was very convenient you were here?"

25

"I was here dropping off my son, Hardy." The Judge deliberately omitted the Detective title, not liking Hardy's tone.

"Okay, okay, don't get your panties in a twist. Just asking. Where's Laura Wilson? I need to talk to her next."

"She's with the kids and staff in the multi-purpose room. Shall I get her?"

"Yes. Now."

Hardy stood where he was, making more notes, as the Judge set off to find Laura. The Judge stuck his head into the multi-purpose room and waved for Laura over the squeals and racket of forty small heads. The kids were busy on the floor, organized in four groups approximately by age and size, and were painting on cardboard boxes, or throwing blocks at each other, or playing in solitary mode with a truck or a doll, depending on their age, sex and disposition.

Ralphie seemed in destruction mode this morning, running his truck with amazing force into a friend's car, toppling the car and almost the friend with the impact, accompanying the planned accident with the guttural noises of a small bear. The Judge waved but there was no acknowledgement. Apparently, it was already not cool to have your dad waving at you while you played with your peers.

"Judge, can you come with me to talk to the police?" asked Laura.

"I've got business to take care of Laura. I really can't stay."

"Oh please, please, Judge I'm so nervous. Just ten minutes more Judge, I beg you. The police are so… intimidating. And after that awful letter, I just need you there for support. Please."

"What letter?"

"You haven't seen the letter?"

"No."

"Well, I'm sure you will. Please Judge. Just ten minutes more."

"Okay, Laura. But let's go do this quickly, get it over with."

They walked back outside, the Judge noting a news crew now setting up across the street. Detective Hardy listened to Laura's story with an expressionless face, taking down careful notes. Was there a hint of underlying animosity in the detective's stance, weight on one leg, leaning forward with the other? The Judge couldn't be sure.

"So, you just walked into the maintenance room and found the body of Mr. Simpson?"

"Yes."

"Is there any other way in?"

"No."

"I've heard there are underground tunnels under the school leading all over. Is that right?"

"No."

"You came in through the door from the hall?"

"Yes."

"Was the door locked?"

"Yes."

"You used your key to get in?"

"Yes."

"So why would you think Mr. Simpson was in the maintenance room if the door was locked?"

"The door opens out into the hall. It's set up to be self-locking. Once the door closes, to open the door from either side requires a key. If Mr. Simpson had gone in there, I knew the door would be locked behind him."

"Who besides you has a key?"

"Mr. Simpson."

"The deceased?"

Laura shuddered. "Yes. And Harry, my brother."

"No one else?"

"No."

"When you stepped into the room, you couldn't see the body?"

"No."

"What made you go to the window in the back and peek around the shelves?"

"I don't know."

"Was it because you already knew he was hanging there?"

"No."

"Then why?"

"I don't know."

"That's not good enough."

The Judge said, "Officer, Miss Wilson has answered the question. You're not allowed to badger her."

Hardy turned to glare at the Judge. "You her lawyer?"

"For the moment I guess I am."

"So, she needs a lawyer?"

"Everyone's entitled to have a lawyer if they wish, and Miss Wilson is entitled to be free from badgering by the police."

"And that's what you do? You're a lawyer?"

"Yes."

"It's very convenient Ms. Wilson's lawyer just happens to be here, don't you think?"

"I explained that."

"From the point where you exited your car this all sounds very unusual to me. Not just a normal drop off of a kid. Your presence here during school hours, unsupervised by anyone, is troubling. I'm putting you on the list."

"What list?"

"The list our department is developing of those potentially connected to the things going on at The Strand Pre-School."

"The what? What things are going on?"

"You heard me. I'm done here. But I expect to see you, Judge, at the police station, this afternoon at four-thirty sharp. I don't like the way this looks. Particularly since Mr. Simpson was scheduled to talk to us this afternoon about things."

"Things?"

"Things, counselor. I'm sure your client will fill you in, but you seem *intimately* involved already."

There was almost a sneer in the detective's voice. What the devil was going on?

"Your first name isn't Oliver by chance, is it Hardy?"

"How'd you know that?"

"Got a partner with a first name of Stan?"

This earned a glare from the detective. He'd apparently heard this before. He snapped his flip-book closed, pulled at his coat to cover his paunch, spun on his heel, and stalked off to his cruiser. The Judge turned to Laura for an explanation.

Laura's face had turned white. She covered her face with her hands and began to cry.

CHAPTER 5

The Judge offered his hanky, only slightly used, to Laura, and then put his arm around her and slowly led her back to her small office, tucked just inside the entrance hall of the school. She collapsed behind an old battered desk that looked World War I vintage, stacked with piles of papers and bills in an order only she knew, sinking into a rickety office chair, wiping her eyes, trying to regain her composure.

"Thanks for standing beside me, Judge. Some days it's almost impossible here."

"Money problems?"

"Always." Laura gave him a faint smile. "I almost wish it was the old days again, when we were an item. Remember? Jesus, we had some fun."

"We did, Laura. But we wore each other out in the process."

"You're right there, Judge. We used to get together and then I'd walk bow-legged for a week. The firehouse used to make a lot of fun of me. Said I was no good sliding down poles after a visit with you."

She gave him a soft smile.

"So, what's the problem here, Laura, besides your dead body? Money?"

"You've got part of it, Judge. There's lots of competition now providing the services we provide. And it's difficult to find and keep good people, caring people, experienced people, people we can trust with

31

our children. Other pre-schools, desperate to stay afloat, have sharply discounted prices, initiating a price war. A race to the bottom and bankruptcy in my view. And some parents don't pay; they're slippery, or broke, sliding out of the bottom of the middle class into poverty as this recession grinds them down. We have an evaporating pool of parents who can afford our services on one hand, and ravenous competitors on the other. Some days it just seems too much. And now this. Our parents will be horrified. A dead body on our campus."

"What about the 'things' Detective Hardy was talking about, Laura? What are these 'things'?"

Laura gave a sigh, sinking lower in her chair, flushed now, avoiding the Judge's eyes. Finally, she said in a low voice, "It's the letter."

"What letter?"

Laura rummaged through a corner stack of papers and then threw a form letter across the desk for the Judge to read, anger flaring in her eyes.

The letter was on official stationary of the Ocean Hill Police Department. It read:

Dear Parent,

This Department is conducting a criminal investigation involving child molestation. Harry Wilson, an employee of The Strand Pre-School, was detained and questioned two weeks ago by this Department, and subsequently released for lack of evidence, pending our further investigation.

This inquiry is necessary for a complete investigation.

Records indicate that your child is currently, or was recently, a student at The Strand Pre-School. Please question your child to see if he or she has been witness to any crime, or has been a victim.

Our investigation thus far suggests that possible criminal acts might have occurred. These may have included oral sex, fondling of genitals, buttocks or chest area, and/or even sodomy, possibly committed under pretense of taking the child's temperature. Also, photos may have been taken of children without their clothing. Any information from your child that they may have seen Harry Wilson leave a classroom with a child, or seen Harry Wilson tie up a child, is important.

Please complete the enclosed questionnaire and return it at once. Please keep this investigation strictly confidential, and do not discuss it outside your family. Do not contact or discuss this with Harry Wilson, or any owner, employee or other person connected with The Strand Pre-School.

If you are concerned that something might have happened with your child, we are suggesting parents accept a free counseling session for their child offered by Dr. George Gibson, an experienced therapist, and the director of the Minor's Refuge for Change, an organization that specializes in helping abused children.

There is no evidence to indicate that the management of the strand pre-school had any knowledge of this situation, and no detrimental information concerning the operation of the school has been discovered. Also, no other employee of the school is under investigation for any criminal act.

William O'Neal,
Chief of Police,
Ocean Hill Police Department.

CHAPTER 6

The Judge sat back in his chair, stunned, starring at the letter for a time. Then he looked at Laura.

"It's all bullshit, Judge. None of it's true. Poor Harry. My brother hasn't done anything wrong. This is all based on the single complaint of one dad, who frankly has a drinking problem and is unstable. I'm at my wits' end about what to do about it."

"I didn't get a copy of this letter."

"It was posted in the mail last night. A friend in the police department faxed me a copy early this morning. She didn't think it was right, what they're doing. Christ, Judge, what am I going to do?"

"Well, for now, Laura, I don't think there's much you can do, except perhaps send out an explanatory letter of your own. I think you mostly have to wait. See where this goes."

"Bastards. The police are going to destroy my school."

"I'm so sorry, Laura. You're right. It's not fair."

They sat silent after that, Laura staring at the letter, which lay face down on her desk, the Judge watching her with a somber look. The Judge finally got up, gave Laura a big hug that lasted just a tad too long, then turned and left, leaving her there staring off into space.

The Judge spent several hours at his Venice office preparing for an upcoming arbitration. He liked the work. It was a lot like judging, but as an arbitrator you didn't have to stay in a stuffy courtroom all day. Besides, the pay was considerably better. At least it was when you could get gigs, which, unfortunately, seemed few and far between right now. Competition was tough, as it was for everything in L.A.

The Judge left Venice at four o'clock, and at four-thirty pulled into parking next to the Ocean Hill Police Station, a boxy complex on the corner of Valley Boulevard and 15th Street, three stories, counting the lower level built deep into the ground for the jail with its long Perp Walk Ramp running up from the bowels of the jail to street level. People released from jail were forced to walk up the Perp Ramp, a trek of shame, guilty or not. A small tower hung above station's entrance, like a prison's guard tower, airy, with glass windows.

The Judge announced his presence to the pretty clerk in uniform behind the bullet-proof glass window and spent ten minutes reading miscellaneous pamphlets and leaflets about the city and its government until Detective Hardy appeared from behind a tall partition inside the station and pushed a button, buzzing open a bullet-proof glass door. The Judge stepped into the inner sanctum and extended a hand to shake, which Hardy reluctantly took with a sour expression. Hardy gestured for the Judge to follow him back further into the depths of the building, down a narrow hall with small conference rooms to either side, doors standing open, all empty. Hardy chose the last one in the back, holding the door open for the Judge, no smile. All business.

The room was sparse: drab grey walls, no pictures, a glass mirror down one side, no doubt two-way. There was a small table with two chairs, everything with rounded edges, lightweight unbreakable plastic, a single heavy metal ring anchored to the floor beneath one chair. It was intimidating, as it was supposed to be.

"Sit down there, Judge. I want you to take me step by step through your entire morning, starting with your getting out of bed, and ending with our discussion in front of The Strand Pre-School."

The Judge rattled on about his morning, getting up, kissing his wife goodbye, finding he was stuck with dropping Ralphie off at pre-school, the long line at The Strand drop-off, Laura Wilson's plea for help, his trip to the maintenance room, running into Jeff Simpson's foot, his check of body temperature. How he'd escorted Laura Wilson out, running into Harry Wilson, her brother. His return to take one more look at the room and the body out of curiosity. His calling of emergency services, and his squat outside on the curb until the police arrived.

Hardy sat in a stony silence, listening, occasionally making a note, rarely taking his eyes off the Judge. The Judge felt like a mouse under the stern gaze of a hungry cat.

"Was that your big fuckin' footprint in the puddle beneath the body?"

"Err… I suppose it could have been."

"Great, just great. We know what's going on at that school, Judge."

"What?"

"You've seen the Chief's letter?"

"Yes. Now I have. Laura, Miss Wilson, showed it to me after you left."

"Then you know…"

"I know what was in the letter. I have no reason to believe anything like that is going on at The Strand."

"Except for this morning's homicide."

"Except for this morning's death, which has the earmarks of a suicide."

"Jeffrey Simpson was supposed to come in here just about now. Sit in the same chair you're sitting in. Spill the beans on The Strand school and the awful child abuse going on there."

"He told you he observed child abuse at the school?"

"His intent was clear when we talked on the phone."

"That's evasive. Did he specifically say there was child abuse going on at the school?"

"Well, no. But he would have. He just didn't get the chance."

"You don't know that for sure."

"I know quite a lot for sure. Simpson's death is so very convenient for certain parties connected with the school, perhaps even you."

"Me?"

"Yes." Hardy rose out of his chair now, meaty fists on the table, leaning over into the Judge's face. The classic stance of a bully.

"I looked up the reports on your running around Silicon Beach without your pants one night a few years ago. The word is you should have been charged with indecent exposure, put on our sex offender list. But our prior D.A. was a golfing buddy, so I'm told. And the whole thing got quashed. I'm not a big fan of Law Enforcement by Exception, Judge."

"You've got your facts wrong, Hardy. I was fleeing in the water for my life at the time. You can confirm that with the Santa Monica Police Chief or look at the court records on the resulting arrests thanks to my intervention in the case."

"I'll just do that, Judge. For now, you're a prime candidate for our list of perverts at The Strand Pre-School."

"So, your minds made up, Hardy? No jury, no trial, no process of accumulation of verifiable facts, no chance for an accused to meet and question his accusers, cross examine witnesses, or present the accused's side of the story with the aid of legal counsel?"

"You perverts don't deserve any of that. It's just a waste of time and money. I've seen the evidence reports from some of the children. In the old days we'd have watched while the community just took you people out and strung you up in the trees."

"So why haven't these 'people' you claim are perverts been charged?"

"Off the record, and I'll swear I never said this, Ocean Hill has a chicken-shit Chief of Police, weak and ineffectual. But the County D.A.'s going to take charge; get the job done for everyone. She'll wipe that smart-ass smile right off your face, Judge."

"I think we're done here, Hardy. Unless you and your Chief want to charge me with something. In fact, I think I'd like to meet your Chief now."

"What?"

"You heard me. I want to meet the Chief."

"He's probably not in."

"Why don't we find out?"

Hardy was flustered, his face turning a slight pink, no doubt wishing he'd not been so candid in sharing his opinions about his Chief. No longer the bully, he'd flipped in an instant to the worried subordinate. Muttering under his breath about smart-ass attorneys, he escorted the Judge out of the little interview office and back along the hall, pointing him across the outer bullpen to another door.

CHAPTER 7

The Judge saw a frosted door on the far side of the room, marked: Chief'. In front of the door sat a watchdog clerk at a desk, a large Asian girl with tattoo markings on both meaty arms, perhaps Polynesian. She stopped mid-stroke filling out a form and watched the Judge suspiciously as he approached. He identified himself and asked to see the Chief. He could feel Hardy quietly fuming behind him across the bullpen.

"What's your business with the Chief?" she asked.

"I'm a concerned citizen. I was at The Strand Pre-School this morning and I discovered the body there. I'm also a member of the California Bar and a retired judge. I'd like some answers on what's going on. Detective Hardy has been less than forthcoming."

"Sit down over there." She pointed to three chairs lined up perhaps ten feet from her desk, then reached for her phone. She spoke softly into the phone for a minute, too softly for the Judge to hear from his quarantined seat, frowned unpleasantly at what she heard, set the phone down and pointed with her thumb over her shoulder, indicating the Judge could move past her to the Chief's door. As he did so, the door opened and the Chief came out to greet the Judge.

"I'm Chief of Police Bill O'Neal," said a tall, slow-talking man, early sixties, with penetrating dark eyes. He had a tan leathery face from walking too many beats in his early days, and the quick smile and warm handshake of a politician, attributes required to move up the ranks and maintain one's position at the top of the police pyramid in the satellite cities surrounding L.A.

The Judge was shown into a large office. A battered bookshelf to the left was filled with the California Penal Code, various treatises on criminal law, and a surprising number of law books. The plaques on the wall to the right explained, declaring William O'Neal the holder of a Juris Doctorate from Michigan Law School, a member of its Law Review, and Order of the Coif. There were also various civic awards and plaques, a picture of a young Bill O'Neal with members of his unit in Vietnam, and a group shot of Bill, a woman, likely his longtime wife, and four adults in their mid-thirties with spouses and a spattering of grandchildren in varying ages and poses.

O'Neal pointed to a chair in front of a battered desk, and settled comfortably into his own oversized office chair, leaning back, pinning his arms behind his head, relaxed but alert. The Judge felt quality here.

The Judge explained his presence at The Stand Pre-School earlier in the day, his longtime friendship with Laura Wilson, her discovery of Jeff's body, the letter she'd shown him alleging child abuse at the school, and his desire to know what the hell was going on.

O'Neal leaned further back in his chair, considering his words, careful now. Then he spoke.

"Sorry if there's been an inconvenience, Judge. I was in your courtroom several times when you were on the bench. You were tough but fair. I liked that. Wish you'd been re-elected."

"Water under the bridge," said the Judge, matching O'Neal's soft smile. "Can you tell me what's going on?"

"I will, but off the record. No repeat of what I say to the press, or anyone."

"Fair enough."

"We have a complaining witness. Says his four-year-old daughter was sexually abused at The Strand Pre-School by Harry Wilson. The guy went to the D.A. about it, not us. The D.A. initially kicked it back here for further investigation. We brought Harry Wilson in for questioning. Detained him over night, but we couldn't shake his story.

We've been conducting an ongoing investigation since. Interviews of the children have been conducted by a therapist, Dr. George Gibson, the Director of MRC, The Minor's Refuge for Change, a sincere guy, and very experienced. We've had a medical doctor examine several children. Results have been mixed. My gut tells me something was going on, but what, and how to prove it, those are the questions. Some kids say they were sexually abused by Harry Wilson, Laura Wilson, and other strangers at The Strand. Parents are going ballistic. But the extent of the abuse and its nature is unclear. Parents in our community have been demanding Harry Wilson and Laura Wilson's immediate arrest."

"But you haven't arrested them?"

"No."

"And the letter?"

"That may not have been my best move. We have a limited budget and frankly this case is bigger than our little police department is equipped to handle. But the City Council and local parents pressed me to get the news out. We don't have the resources to go knock on everybody's door. So, the Council argued the letter was needed. After trying to talk them out of the idea, the City Council essentially ordered me to send the letter out. So, I did."

"And what's happening now?"

"This is entirely off the record. I don't know for sure what really happened at The Strand. My detectives have so far found no corroborating evidence. None of the suspects have copped a plea, no mea culpa, no one got drunk and bared his soul. We've found no photographs, no videos, no props, no witnesses, no tunnels. If everything the kids said happened, it looks like the perfect crime. Hell, even the Mafia has snitches."

"So, what's next, Bill?"

"As I said, as a department we've been under intense pressure both from the parents and from the D.A. to make arrests. As you probably know, Nancy Aragon, the D.A., is running for re-election. She's now decided she wants this case brought immediately. She wants an arrest so badly she can taste it. She's been calling me daily, and routinely getting mad and hanging up after arguing I'm soft on crime. Aragon even had her office draw up an arrest complaint for Harry Wilson and Laura Wilson under our Department's name, and brought it to me to sign. I refused. Told her there's no corroboration that a crime's been committed. I don't see enough so far to charge anyone."

"So that's where it stands?"

"No. I wish it were. But the D.A.'s recently stopped calling. And I just heard this morning, that she's gone around me. She's taken the case to the Los Angeles County Grand Jury. You know how that works; the Grand Jury will rubber stamp practically any indictment request the D.A. brings. That's all I know right now."

"Wow. What about your Detective Hardy? He dragged me down here and accused me of being a pervert. He's something of a bully."

"I apologize for that. Hardy can get a little over-bearing at times. But he's been here a long time, he's well liked, and he does a good job at detecting. He and I have been working on some of his anger management issues. I wish I had enough staff so I could take him off The Strand Pre-School investigation."

"Why's that?"

"I wouldn't bring it up with him. He gets really upset. But last year Hardy's five-year-old daughter attended the The Strand Pre-School."

CHAPTER 8

The Judge pulled up his driveway in Palos Verdes and into his garage about six o'clock. As he switched off the engine his bride Katy was at his car window. He didn't have a chance to open his door. She was there, waving through the glass the same form letter he'd read in Laura's office, her face red and blotchy. She must have been crying.

"You won't believe this, Judge. You won't believe what they've been doing to our Ralphie and to the other young children at that damn Pre-School of yours. Look! Just look! It's unbelievable."

"Now honey, you shouldn't believe everything you read." He crawled out of the car, wishing his tummy wasn't so big and he was quicker on his feet. Quicker in his head too, so he could more easily deflect what was coming.

"Oh no, Judge. Oh no. This comes directly from the Ocean Hill Police Department. They know what they're talking about."

"I don't think so, Katy. I was at The Strand this morning for a fair amount of time. Mostly sitting in the damn drop-off line. You didn't warn me about that. Anyway, I got re-acquainted with Laura Wilson. When I was growing up she and her parents were friends of my family. I remember her kid brother too, Harry. Laura is the same as I remember, quiet, dedicated to her kids at the school."

"Oh, it's Laura, now, is it?'

"Katy, I can't believe there's any hanky-panky going on at The Strand based on what I saw and what I know about Laura."

"Hanky-panky…. Hanky-panky!" Katy was sputtering now. "Shit, Judge, molestation of my son isn't hanky-panky. Why were you talking to Mistress Laura anyway?" Katy's sensors were now on full alert.

"Err… well, there was a problem."

"A problem? What kind of problem?"

"Well, you know, a problem." The Judge gave her his best boyish grin.

"Turn off that shit-eating grin Judge and tell me about the problem."

"Well… someone died."

"What? At the school? Oh, shit. I knew it, I knew it. How'd they die?"

"Well… he sort of… you know… just died."

"How? Spit it out, Judge."

"He sort of hung himself." The Judge squeezed the words out all at once in a low voice, indistinct, hoping for the best.

"How does someone 'sort of' hang them self? Either you do or you don't."

"Well, it looks like suicide. But there are always questions. There was no note. The police are suspicious and investigating."

"That's it Judge. I'm finding another pre-school."

"This sort of thing can happen anywhere, Katy. It's not the school's fault. And this letter from the police department looks like a smear job if I ever saw one. The school's been a great institution here for thirty years, done good work, has a dedicated staff."

"Not my problem, Judge. Ralphie comes first. Which reminds me. Our little guy said there was a game you wanted to play tonight. Something about movie stars he'd learned at the school." The conversation had carried them inside the house. "Ralphie, come here honey. Tell us about your new game."

The Judge was in deep trouble now and he knew it. "Perhaps we should do this after dinner," he suggested hopefully.

But the little man had heard his name and was excited to show what he'd learned. He came into the kitchen and stood before them, shifting weight back and forth on one leg and then the other with excitement. These days he found it difficult to be still for long, unless he was asleep.

Katy said, "Honey, what was that game you were telling me about. The one you want to play with Daddy?'

"Movie Star."

"How do you play, honey?"

"Well, mostly you just sing a song. Like this:" Ralphie's tweedy little voice burst into the sort of melody only admiring parents could appreciate.

What you say… is what you are… You're a naked movie star." Ralphie giggled.

Katie got her jaw off the ground with some difficulty, then snapped. "Okay, Judge, that's it. Our son can't set a foot in that place again!"

"There're no allegations against Laura Wilson, Katy. If everybody bails based on a silly rumor like this, the school will immediately go broke and disappear. It will be a loss for the community and all the future preschoolers who could benefit from their tradition of teaching and child care, things which have made The Strand Pre-School a pillar of the community.

"This is our son you're talking about, Judge. My baby. Suppose just one more day goes by for Ralphie at the school, and that's the one day he's molested. His whole life ruined. Tomorrow. Molested tomorrow! Because of your bull-headedness."

"Look, Katy, I grew up with Laura Wilson. I've known her for years. Our mothers were in the same bridge club. I can one hundred percent vouch for Laura. She's not a child molester."

"And what about the people around her at that school, Judge? What about the younger brother, Henry, or Harry, or whatever his name is? The one the cops actually arrested but had to let go. Can you guarantee one of them won't molest our Ralphie?"

"Ralphie's in Laura's class. He doesn't see Harry Wilson, or any of the other teachers."

"How can you be so calm about this?"

"There's no evidence, Katy. It's just all rumors and gossip. I don't know Harry Wilson, but I know the family. They'd never be associated with child abuse or molestation. You can't panic like this. We need to ignore these baseless charges, stand by The Strand, and support it."

"Fine, Judge. You take Ralphie tomorrow, then. It's on your head." Katy stormed out of the kitchen, saying she was going shopping over her shoulder, her answer to anything approaching marital stress.

CHAPTER 9

The Judge found himself dropping off Ralphie the next morning after a further short but bitter argument with Katy. Katy even offered to take a vacation day from her post as Palos Verdes High's Senior Counselor to get Ralphie re-situated somewhere else or dropped at her mother's.

The Judge insisted they send Ralphie to the school for another week and see what news develop about the school and its staff. Katy finally ran out of time to argue and had to rush for the door, having made herself late for her counseling job at Palos Verdes High. She was in a bad temper, muttering all the way down the driveway.

And so here the Judge sat again in the damn drop-off line again, twiddling his thumbs and breathing gas fumes. Ralphie sat behind him in the raised car seat, happy enough, making blowing sounds with his lips, perhaps trying to whistle. It was unclear. There seemed a third fewer cars in line. The Chief's letter to the parents had taken its toll,

As Miss Johnsen reached in to unbuckle the boy, the face of Harry Wilson appeared behind her, looking strained, tense, dark blue eyes angrily pinning the Judge. "I want to talk for a minute, Judge." He opened the front passenger seat door and slid in uninvited. "We can park over there."

The Judge reluctantly pulled the car over to the same spot he'd used the day before and killed the engine. He was already behind schedule for a meeting in Venice. But it seemed he had little choice

"Are you screwing my sister again, Judge?"

"What?" The Judge's jaw dropped open, at a loss for words. Finally, he managed, "What are you talking about?"

"My sister has perpetually poor taste in men. She took it very hard when you dumped her before. I don't want her hurt again."

"Harry, we dated briefly, that was all, and it was several years ago. I'm married now, happily so. I have no romantic interest in Laura. Besides, our break-up at the time was a mutual decision."

"That may have been what you thought, but Laura was devastated. She has no sense about whom to trust with her romantic feelings or her body. She keeps attracting and settling for the same kind of men. Immature, self-centered, selfish males who only want one thing. They jump on her, use her, get tired of her, and then jump ship. Leaving me to patch her up and put her back on an even keel."

The Judge bit his tongue, almost literally. He'd be damned if he'd discuss any part of his past relationship with Laura's uppity brother. But he didn't like being put on the defensive. He decided turnabout was fair play.

"I saw the letter, Harry. They're investigating you for child abuse."

"That's a crock of shit, Judge and you know it. One alcoholic dad makes some ridiculous accusation, and suddenly I'm tried, convicted and censured in the press and in the community, without so much as a single piece of evidence. And without a trial. Look at this place, half the children aren't coming today because of that damn letter. We're getting cancellations right and left. This isn't America anymore, it's a Nazi State.

But I want to talk about my sister. Stay away from Laura. If you two are screwing around again, it stops now. Don't interrupt." Harry held up his hand as the Judge tried to intercede. "This is the only warning you get. Touch my sister again and who knows, you might have a serious accident."

With that Harry opened his door and spun out of the car, giving the Judge no time to respond. He slammed the car door shut with such force it rattled the windows and the Judge's teeth, the ones he was now grinding. Harry Wilson stalked off across the front lawn toward The Strand, not looking back.

The Judge stared after Harry for a time, wondering about his anger management issues, wondering if it had been a mistake to let Ralphie go to school here today, wondering what Laura had told Harry about their former relationship, wondering if Harry was suited to be teaching small children in a pre-school environment. Lots and lots of wondering.

CHAPTER 10

The Judge returned home about six, pulling up the driveway and into the garage.

There was a certain chill in the air over dinner, but Katy warmed after, giving him a hug from behind before clearing dishes. She worked into the conversation she had another pre-school she'd like to visit with him at the weekend, one she thought better suited to Ralphie, closer to home, without a drop-off line, and high marks for collaborative play and young child education.

The Judge knew intuitively he may have won a skirmish this morning but he'd lose this war. She considered raising kids in the center of her prerogatives as the female half of their domestic relationship, and although she might politely listen to his ill-considered male advice about parenting Ralphie, in the end she'd do precisely what she wanted. He may as well piss into the wind.

After dinner he settled into his favorite chair, soft brown leather, with scratches and scars from long use, and contours that now just fit his body. He put his feet up on the matching ottoman, gently swishing his heavily iced gin and tonic, Sapphire, and turned on the 85-inch TV, his pride and joy. It was a relaxing way to end a trying day. He flipped to the nine o'clock news.

Then he bolted upright, startled, spilling his generously poured drink across his lap, cursing under his breath at the flood of gin as the newscaster declared in a grim voice.

"More than sixty children from The Strand Pre-School have now told authorities they have been keeping a grotesque secret: Sexual Abuse. Made to appear in pornographic films, fondled, forced to watch the killing and mutilation of small animals calculated to scare the kids into silence."

"Jesus, Christ."

"Two teachers from the school were arrested late this afternoon as a result of a grand jury indictment, unsealed and released this morning: Head Mistress, Laura Wilson and her brother, Harry Wilson. They have been indicted on charges of child abuse perpetuated over a several-year period. There are almost two hundred children suspected of being abused. The children are being interviewed now by the authorities.

We've beat everybody to break this story earlier today, but we feel awful because this is such a sick, sick story to tell."

He flipped to another channel's news in disgust, hoping Katy hadn't overheard. But they were showing video footage of the story. Someone had tipped the press to the arrests and the media was there in force. It was six o'clock in the evening by the time stamp, just the time everyone was home and settling in for dinner when the show began.

There were four police cruisers and a SWAT truck outside Laura's home, their red beacons flashing reds and blues. Police swarmed around the house, holding ugly looking automatic weapons, moving awkwardly in their black, full flak gear, wearing otherworldly helmets. A commander, farther back from the line, strutted around looking self-important in front of the cameras lined up to record the arrest.

The full replay of this footage was peppered with lurid commentary from the newscaster, droning on about the horrendous crimes committed. Laura was led out of her house, her hands cuffed behind her, walking stiffly in a classic perp-walk the authorities so loved. She was deposited on the curb outside her house for a few minutes, carefully positioned between cruisers so gathered neighbors and the news crews could get a good look and photographers could take clean shots. She was dressed in dusty jeans and a vivid red blouse that complemented her hair, but she looked disheveled and angry.

An assigned officer marched over and unceremoniously yanked Laura to her feet, led her to a waiting police car, and roughly pushed her head down as he propelled her into the back seat, hands still cuffed behind, while cameras flashed, clicked and whizzed.

"The school has been involved in secret ritualistic practices involving a 'Goat man' and a Satanic Church," continued the newscaster, *"resulting in the drugging, raping and sodomizing of the small children entrusted to their care."*

The Judge flipped to a third news channel, glad Katy was still in a back bedroom reading Ralphie a story. But the third news channel was also playing the story.

"Therapists have used drawings to cleverly draw out the truth from these poor damaged kids. Here are some of the pictures the kids drew of their teachers." The newscaster displayed several drawings. All were primitive. None were flattering.

A clip of D.A. Nancy Aragon came on, trotting out the allegations she'd obtained from her secret Grand Jury, looking pleased with herself.

"I've indictments for two people, based upon fifty instances of molestation at The Strand Pre-School, with eighteen children identified as victims. We view Harry Wilson and Laura Wilson as dangerous risks to the community and will seek their detention without bail pending trial."

Nancy Aragon had made a name for herself and got herself elected as District Attorney of Los Angeles County three and a half years earlier. She was now up for re-election. The Judge knew there was a determined effort to replace her with a new candidate, funded by well-heeled interests in the County.

Her opponent had raised a considerable war chest and was appearing everywhere speaking on issues surrounding the office, even ahead of his formal declaration of intent to run. Aragon was outmatched in campaign money and in style. But she was hovering around the courthouse whenever a big case was in progress, and then speaking freely to news media afterward. Holding impromptu press conferences, bolstering her reputation and her claim she was tough on crime.

She no doubt had high hopes for The Strand Pre-School Molestation case. An expectation of extensive media coverage, lots of controversy, lots of press conferences where she could pound the table and yet again declare herself stronger on crime enforcement than her opponent. It would be a circus. This case would clearly outshine any other. It was already making headlines on all the networks.

Someone asked the D.A. if this this case would help her current campaign for re-election. *"This demonstrates how unfounded the statements are by my about-to-be opponent in this race, in which he accuses me of being soft on crime*," said Aragon. "*We've got these… people… these 'defendants', dead to rights, and we're going to charge them with all the law allows.*"

The screen returned to the newscaster. The newsman confided he'd talked to one of the Deputy District Attorneys who'd reported, "*drugs are being used to make the children submit. They are given pills, liquids, and shots to make them woozy, drowsy, less likely to resist assault.*"

The Judge flipped back one channel. There the anchor was opining, "*This was literally a Sexual House of Horrors. One little girl told of a game of cowboys and Indians where she took off her clothes and then stood still and had to let everyone touch her. Another little boy asked his mother, 'Mommy, when I die, will the bad memories go away?'*

And why did the children remain silent for so long?" asked the anchor, rhetorically. "*Because they were brainwashed and frightened into silence!*"

The Judge flipped one more channel back. Here the newscaster had turned to the discovery of a body on The Strand Pre-School campus the previous morning. "*The deceased is rumored to have made an appointment with authorities to spill all about goings on at the school and the pedophile ring entrenched there. An appointment his death prevented him from keeping. Although the hanging is an apparent suicide, police are investigating further to determine if foul play was involved.*" Film footage ran, and there was the Judge in glaring video, talking in front of the pre-school to Laura Wilson and the police detective.

The newsman droned on, "*Head Mistress Wilson is in so deep she'd already lawyered up to fend off the police investigators when this video was shot yesterday morning.*" The Judge muttered under his breath at the yellow press journalism, painting Laura guilty without a trial.

CHAPTER 11

The next morning dawned clear and blue, as it usually does in Malaga Cove. The Judge looked out from his breakfast table, high on the hill overlooking the dusty Los Angeles Bowl from downtown to Malibu and beyond, overhanging the giant blue puddle that was the Santa Monica Bay.

The Judge was about to crunch down on a piece of toast, loaded with a way-too-thick layer of orange marmalade, out of sight of Katy of course, deliberately oblivious to his slowly escalating bulk. His cell phone suddenly lit up, peeling off a wolf whistle. The damn cell insisted on self-selecting its own ring tone periodically, punishment for its being left to rattle around in his shirt pocket, to collide now and then with his pen.

"Hello."

Katy quietly walked into the room on his left, some feminine instinct prodding her into earshot of the call.

"Well hello, Laura."

"Yes, I watched the ugly reporting on the news last night. It was totally unfair."

"Yes, Laura, I can talk now."

"Yes, I know where you are right now. Are they treating you okay?"

"How can I help?"

"Well… you see Laura, I'm not a specialist in criminal lawyering. It is a specialty. So, it's not something I would typically take on."

"Well, I understand."

"You definitely need your own counsel and Harry needs his own separate counsel."

"So, cash is really that tight?"

"Sure, I can find a good criminal lawyer for Harry if there is some money to fund his counsel, but what are you going to do?"

"Yes."

"I understand."

"Don't cry. Take some deep breaths. You've got to keep your head up. This will all work out."

"Yes."

"But…"

"You're sure you want me?"

"Tell you what, I'll come up and see you tomorrow morning at the jail. We can talk about it."

The Judge took his pen and jotted an address on the corner of his Wall Street Journal.

"Yes. I know it's unfair."

"You just have to do the best you can. I'll see you in the morning."

The Judge put his cell down, turning to look at Katy, who was picking her jaw up off the floor, shifting her hands onto her hips and slowly moving her head back and forth in disbelief.

"You're not really going to represent that… that… that… ho?"

"I only said we'd talk about it." The Judge was on the defensive and knew it.

"Judge, you can't represent that Laura woman!"

"Why not?"

"Because our son goes to The Strand Pre-School. Because Ralphie may even be abused for all we know. Because she'll ruin your reputation. Because no one will want to hire you again for any legitimate legal work. Because she's a pedophile and belongs in jail. You've seen the news. Because, because... because I don't like her, she's divorced, and rumored to sleep around with married men."

Katy ran out of breath.

"Katy, she's entitled to a presumption of innocence until proven guilty in a court of law. It looks to me like she's being railroaded by a rabid press and a politically motivated D.A. And it's what I do. I'm a lawyer. Guilty or innocent, she's entitled to legal representation and the right to demand the prosecution prove their case before a jury of her peers... if they can."

Katy shook her head again, stomping around the room in frustration.

"Judge just listen to what they're saying. They have her dead to rights. She's an awful person. And she may have harmed our son. The police wouldn't have arrested her unless they'd had solid proof. And the D.A. has indicted her. A grand jury has concluded she's guilty. Their case is solid or it'd never have gotten this far. Haven't you been listening to the news?"

"Katy, the press has launched a smear campaign to sell newspapers and bring eyes to their network news. They're essentially convicting poor Laura in the press. Without a trial. Without due process. And our grandstanding D.A., caught in the middle of a tough re-election campaign, is fanning the flames, extracting every ounce of notoriety she can squeeze out of the case. It's totally unfair. How in the hell is Laura going to get an impartial jury that can sit and judge the evidence with these salacious and unproven allegations spread all over the news?"

"You can't blame the press for this, Judge. The news media is just doing their job. The public has a right to know. The press is fulfilling their responsibility to get the news out. The Los Angeles Grand Jury looked at the evidence and concluded Laura Wilson's guilty. And she is. She's guilty as hell. You know it, I know it, shit the whole town knows it. It's all people are talking about.

And she may have ruined our son. You better not even think about taking this case. You're going to put your family first, and you're not going to drag us through Hell just because you like the thrill of behaving… behaving the way you always behave."

With that Katy stormed from the kitchen in a huff. It was amazing how much control Katy presumed she could exert once she had a child. All decisions and all actions were subservient to protection of the child. He supposed it was inbred in the female of the specie; or perhaps just in modern 21st century women.

He didn't know. And it didn't matter. The decision on whom he would represent, and why, would stay solely with him, regardless of any domestic flap. But now he'd lost his appetite for the marmaladed toast. Damn.

The Judge looked at Annie, the golden retriever who'd been with him as a puppy, a domestic relationship that predated Katy. Annie had wandered into the kitchen during the argument to see what the trouble was in the nest. The Judge was exasperated. Perhaps he was looking to Annie for female support. He got none. Annie looked him up and down, sniffed, and trotted off after Katy, clarifying her feelings on the matter.

The Judge reached for the newspaper, still folded in its wrapper on the table where Katy had deposited it. He de-sacked it. The front-page headline declared in bold type:

KIDDY PORN RING OUTTED IN OCEAN HILL...!!!

The Judge read the story with disgust, noting the word "alleged" was only used once. It weaved the findings of the Grand Jury and the concerns intimated in the Ocean Hill Police Department Form letter into a scenario of child molestation, pornography, and devil worship, damning Harry Wilson and Laura Wilson for acts against children, against nature and against God. There was also mention of the suspicious death of the janitor on The Strand Pre-School campus, which the police were treating as linked to the heinous crimes on children committed there.

The Judge gave a big sigh, settling in at his breakfast table with his view, his paper, his coffee and his discarded toast, but now feeling dismal. Wondering why he'd ever been talked into marriage. It wasn't a man's natural state. At least not if you were a loner of sorts. He almost preferred his solitude, quiet and peaceful. What was that old song from My Fair Lady?... How did it go? *Let a woman in your life…*

CHAPTER 12

Forty-five minutes later Katy re-appeared, trailed by Annie the Dog and then Ralphie. They made a small procession of it, traipsing into the kitchen, Katy in full make up now, tear streaks gone, and fresh cover up applied, the Golden with her tail arched high above her hindquarters in a feathery circle, both looking grim. Ralphie making a dash for under the table to chase an ant he'd spotted.

"Okay, Judge. Let's try and have a rational conversation about this, keep the emotion out. Why don't you go first? Why is it so important for you to get involved in this case? And what about freedom of the press, and the public's right to know? How can you disparage those constitutional rights?"

The Judge sat up straighter in his chair, putting aside his newspaper. This was more like it. Nothing like a good historical lecture to clear the air. And he did love a good lecture, most always only if he was the one giving it.

"It starts in the middle ages, Katy."

"What?"

Annie the Dog mimicked Katy's startled look. Ralphie looked up from under the table momentarily, then put his nose down an inch off the floor, still chasing his ant.

"You have to go back in history to understand. Before the Norman Invasion of England, local Saxon

custom and law provided for weekly Moot Courts.
These were held in the open and local Freemen
participated as both judge and jury. Complaints of all
sorts were brought and aired publicly. Disputants were
given the opportunity of make up or work out a
compromise. If none could be had, the Freeman would
decide who was guilty, or liable, and punishment was
meted out."

As the Judge continued his lecture, Ralphie
slowly, slowly, chased his ant into the next room.

"The Moot Court served as a social gathering, a
place to hear the news of the town, a place to satisfy
public curiosity about topical crimes and disputes. It
also served to reassure the populace that justice was
being dispensed fairly and not in a way to advantage the
elite. Moot Court served as a forum for venting group
anxiety, hostility and other concerns, acting as a safety
valve to release community steam."

"So, the press could fully report the
proceedings."

"Yes. But the reporting came from the
evidence presented at Moot Court trial where there was
a presumption of innocence. These two policy
concerns, somewhat in opposition to each other, were
embodied in the First and Sixth Amendments. The
Sixth gives an accused the right to a trial by an impartial
jury. And the First assures freedom of the press,
making the press the people's monitor of the
government's actions."

"So, there you are, Judge. The press has a right
to know and report."

"Well yes… and maybe. In the past we didn't
have so many ways to spread the news far and wide.

These days, in trials of national notoriety, particularly involving murder, mystery, society, and sex, the result is pervasive and continuous national media treatment in newspapers, magazines, radio, television, cable and the internet, well ahead of the trial. In the old days, the defendant could request a change of venue, moving to a different county where people weren't familiar with the case. But in high profile cases it's no longer possible. What has served in the past as an adequate protection for the defendant has eroded until today, what with aggressive reporting and journalistic investigations by news outlets, amateur cell phone video, and the far flung coverage through the internet, not to mention angry bloggers, cases of public notoriety are carried far and wide. It makes it impossible to find an untainted jury."

"Come on, Judge. Even I know that criminal defense attorneys say privately that most of their clients are guilty. Their job is just to game the system."

"That may be, Katy, but that's not the point. Everyone is supposed to be 'presumed' innocent, until 'proven' guilty in a court of law."

"I know all about your court of law and its rules of evidence, Judge. But those rules often preclude getting at the real facts of a matter. Look at the 'Me Too' movement. All those women sexually abused, molested, raped, discriminated against for refusing sexual favors. It's been going on forever. Things never get better unless there's a way to shine a light on it. The press and the internet have done that. They've shined that light."

"They've shined something. And look at the careers and lives ruined by the allegations publicly made in the 'Me Too' movement blasted across the news media and the internet. It results in firings and departures by prominent people without any judicial process vetting the claims of those who have alleged sexual abuse, harassment or insensitivity. News stories designed to be provocative and sell news. Without due process to establish what really happened under our system of jurisprudence."

"The press have done their due diligence and their investigations. And when they've found credible sources to support allegations, they've blasted the perpetuators. And there's been too many of them for you to deny the problem of sexual harassment exists."

"I don't deny the problem exists, Katy. But is every accused person automatically guilty? Aren't problems about assumptions of guilt at the root of why certain groups of people are disproportionately and wrongfully convicted of crimes? Shouldn't there be a minimum standard of proof before punishment? Is it fair to treat everybody against whom an allegation has been made as a criminal, even if criminal trial proceedings haven't concluded, or even begun?"

"Yes. If credible sources establish a woman was raped, or abused, or blackmailed into sex, the perps should hang." Katy folded her arms across her chest and raised her chin, glaring at the Judge again.

"Perhaps my problem is with the concept of 'credible sources', Katy. The word of choice today seems to be 'credible'. Reported by this 'credible' source or backed up by other 'credible' sources. But I don't know what the hell 'credible' means."

"These Wilson scum-bags deserved to go to jail, Judge! How can you not see that? Miss Laura two-sheets and her brother, what they've done is awful."

"Katy... Katy... Katy, we don't know that. You're not supposed to judge someone guilty until there's been a fair trial and a person's been found guilty by their peers. An accused is entitled to a presumption of innocence. And the press is not supposed to pound a stake into the accused's heart based on unsupported assertions, secret sources, disputed facts and so-called credible evidence no one has seen. This country is becoming a country of vigilante justice, promulgated by the press."

Katy stopped and took a big breath. "Okay, Judge, I understand what you're saying. And a part of me believes it, in theory. But the other part of me is Ralphie's mom. What if they've done something awful to our Ralphie? What if they've injured him for life? What are we going to do? I'm just sick with thoughts of what perhaps happened."

"I don't believe Ralphie was molested."

"But you don't know, Judge. You can't be sure."

"I'm sure. Laura would never do something like that. She and her brother are entitled to a fair trial before an unbiased jury. And the press should be muzzled until after that trial occurs."

"Judge, this is Ralphie you're talking about. Our only son. You can't be sure. We must pull him out of The Strand right now. Not another day there; and hope we've done it in time."

The Judge sighed. "Alright, Katy, you point is well taken. I don't want to take chance. It spells the economic end of The Strand Pre-School. I'm sure everyone will pull their kid out of the school. The business enterprise known as The Strand Pre-School is toast. But I do want to make sure my old friend, Laura Wilson, gets a fair trial."

Katy's face was turning pink. "Oh, so Laura is an 'old friend' now, huh Judge?"

Jesus, Katy suspects, mused the Judge, sure he was now looking guilty as hell. He let his face slip into his best boyish charm look, hoping it might help.

Katy and Annie the Dog looked at him with the same unforgiving disdain they'd used earlier, then they turned in unison and marched back toward the bedroom without a further word.

CHAPTER 13

The door chimes went off, cascading bells through the house. The Judge rolled himself out of bed and staggered down the hall under the weight of his hastily grabbed robe, across the cold living room floor in bare feet, and opened the Italian carved front door, muttering to himself as he looked at his watch, *"Seven thirty-five in the morning for Christ sakes."*

A chipper looking fellow was standing on his front porch, short, stout, mid-forties, with a greying beard clipped short but running into side burns up his cheeks. Bright brown eyes stared out at the Judge through Coke-like glasses with intelligence, but the broad smile pasted on his face made the Judge cautious. He wore a tweed jacket in autumn browns over a pale blue shirt, no tie, tan slacks, and brown loafers' sans socks. The Judge found it difficult to trust anyone over thirty who went around without socks.

"Hi. You must be the Judge."

"And if I am?'

"I'm Bradford Jones, with The Los Angeles Daily Mirror, here to get your story." He produced a flip notebook from his back pocket as he spoke, and a pen magically appeared in his hand, perhaps from up his sleeve.

"What story?" asked the Judge, feeling his blood pressure rising. This guy was worse than a real estate agent.

"You're named as one of the 'perverts of interest' on the Ocean Hill Police Department's list, and I'm here to get your response to placement of your name on their list." He lifted his pen to the notebook and looked at the Judge expectantly.

The Judge opened his mouth to speak, but for the first time in his life no words came out. He was literally speechless.

Pulling himself together, the Judge used his best 'from the bench judge-voice,' the one that made his whole courtroom shake with trepidation back in the old days; attorneys, clerk bailiff, and visitors all, when he was unhappy about some occurrence in his private fiefdom. Low, guttural, menacing and powerful, it was a verbal assault that left few unintimidated. Of course, this time his words weren't as elegant as they'd been back in the day.

"Get the fuck off my porch!"

The Judge padded back to bed, fuming, crawled in next to Katy and cuddled up for warmth, but he couldn't sleep. He finally got up and wandered out and down to get the papers at the bottom of the driveway. He liked to grab them before Katy rolled over them in her car in her last-ditch rush to get to the high school and her counseling office on time. Some mornings his cherished papers were churned to mush as Katy bolted backward down the driveway in a panic.

He opened the local paper to see the story of The Strand Pre-School and the death of Jeffrey Simpson again spread across the front page. There was a picture of a dejected Laura Wilson with hair frazzled and arms cuffed behind her, sitting on the curb in front of her home. The story parroted what had been said on the news the evening before.

He turned the front page and stared at page three inside, a full-page ad declaring one newsroom was on top of The Strand child-abuse story. The ad was dramatized with the image of a large and battered teddy bear, one eye missing. its stuffing falling out, and the question, "What did they do to our little children?" Further back in the paper the story continued with pictures of Laura and her brother, describing their personal backgrounds in unflattering terms.

The media was running a blitz on the story for sure. It made him ill.

The Judge poured a lot of coffee in and got himself together. Later in the morning he made several calls on behalf of Harry Wilson looking for a defense attorney. It was more difficult then he'd anticipated to locate a seasoned criminal lawyer willing to wade into the case. Faced with the onslaught of publicity, no one wanted to represent Harry Wilson against charges of child abuse. Finally, he contacted Barney Malone, an charming yet crusty criminal lawyer he'd watched from the bench when he was pinch hitting and had to sit the criminal calendar. Barney was always busy. But he liked longshots and he loved the law.

After two futile calls and one missed exchanged, he reached Barney.

"A friend of mine needs help, Barney."

"Criminal help?"

"Yep."

"How criminal?"

"Child molestation."

There was a long silence. Barney was no fool. Finally, he said, "The Wilsons?"

"Yes. Harry Wilson."

"How come you're calling a broken-down defense lawyer like me, Judge? Why don't you do it yourself? Or you must have plenty of blue-suede shoe boys to turn to."

"Harry Wilson doesn't have significant liquid assets."

"And his case is spread all over the TV and the press. No one wants to touch it. Am I right?"

"You're always right, Barney. That's why my first thought was of you."

"Who's representing the sister, Lorie or Lona or something like that?"

"Laura Wilson. I am."

Barney whistled into the phone. "Wow, I get to be co-counsel with the Judge. I'll do it. Just to watch you sweat it out in a real man's game, criminal law." Barney cackled. "Did she do it, this Laura?"

"No."

"You're sure?"

"I know her well."

"How well, Judge? Thought you got married?"

"I am married. I knew her before."

"Well?"

"Just a friend, Barney? You always were a dirty old man."

"Which is why I qualify to defend a child

molestation case, Judge?"

"Laura Wilson's innocent, Barney. I'm certain of it."

"It'll be a tough case to defend. The D.A.'s loaded for bear; she has a re-election campaign to win. And I heard Superior Court Judge Ferguson has been assigned to the case. He's up for re-election too. Ferguson can't afford to be seen as soft on crime. Plus, whoever the jury is, they will already be conditioned to find the Wilsons guilty given the way the press is playing up this case."

"Just the kind of longshot you like, Barney."

"Shit, you know me too well, Judge. Does Harry
Wilson have assets to liquidate to pay an attorney like me for my time?"

"Some. Won't be enough. You may have to short your fees a little."

"So, he can't pay in full, he's being tried in the press, the D.A.'s gunning for him, the Superior Court Judge won't cut the defense any slack, and whoever takes on the defense is going to be painted by the community with the social stigma of a child molester sympathizer."

"I always knew you were a quick study, Barney. But look at the publicity you'll get. Think of the joy it'll give you to twist the D.A.'s tail. It'll be an adventure."

"You sure know how to sell a girl a good time, Judge. You haven't changed. Are they at County?"

"Yes."

"Okay. I'll go have a chat with Mr. Harry Wilson.

See how the chemistry feels. If you're right and they're being railroaded, it's my kind of case. It's the reason we became lawyers, Judge."

Satisfied he'd done his best by Laura's brother, the Judge hung up. He ambled into his study for more mundane work on a legal dispute he'd been hired to arbitrate, settling behind his ancient desk in front of the window and the view. The sea was a deep blue, a few fluffy clouds overhead reflecting the orange rays of the sun onto the sea's surface below. He never tired of the view. Sometimes it seemed the only constant in this hectic life.

Later in the day Barney called back and said he'd been retained by Harry Wilson and was looking forward to partnering up with the wily Judge on a coordinated defense. The Judge took a deep breath, looked at Katy, who was eavesdropping again over his shoulder and now shaking her head violently 'No'.

"Great, Barney, it'll be like old times again."

Katy turned around and stomped from the room again.

CHAPTER 14

"Since so many of the children have said they were photographed, the FBI has been called in and is looking for sales of photos of unclad children from The Strand Pre-School. Prosecutors say an additional thirty people have been placed under investigation, but declined to give names.

Film footage ran again of the Judge talking in front of the pre-school to Laura Wilson and the police detective the morning of Jeffrey's death. The reporter, Bradford Jones, droned on, naming the Judge as the Wilson lawyer in their video, using the Judge's legal name, and explaining he liked to be known as 'the Judge'.

"The Judge, huh? The guy was thrown off the bench some years ago. The Judge is a man of less than spotless reputation and has been put on the short list of people of interest, targeted for further investigation by the police as they grapple with these heinous crimes and their aftermath."

"Son of a bitch. By God I'll sue that Bradford Jones. What a cheap shot." The Judge was ranting now.

Katy had quietly risen in the bed beside him. He belatedly sensed her alert presence, clamped his jaws shut in mid-rant, and leaped from the bed to shut the TV off. He hoped she hadn't heard the TV newscaster. But she had.

75

"See," she said in a bitter voice, "I told you so, Judge. You're just so damn bull-headed you won't listen. You've made a terrible mistake agreeing to represent this Laura Wilson woman."

She got up, put on her robe, shook her head at the Judge in disgust, and went off to feed Annie the Dog, who was whining in the kitchen that it was time for her breakfast.

The Judge stumbled out of bed and off to the bathroom for a shower, lamenting the steady drumbeat of TV, radio and print media pounding the Wilsons into the ground. Dressed, he could smell fresh coffee and followed the scent to the breakfast room. He found Katy hunched over the morning paper at the small table, reading another scathing article about the Wilsons and The Strand Pre-School. It'd been a bad night for Katy. She had circles under her eyes from tossing and turning in her sleep. She'd even disturbed the Judge's sleep, something difficult to do.

There was a sudden yelp and movement under his feet. Shit! He'd stepped on the dog's tail again. Annie had a habit of sprawling across doorway passages, or in the middle of the floor in rooms like the kitchen and the breakfast room, making it difficult to get around.

The animal turned to look at him, a silent accusation in her eyes. She'd been mistreated again, and she was keeping score. She sauntered over to the other side of the kitchen, nose and tail in the air, and plopped down, hoping for no further disturbance of her nap.

"I'm glad you're up, Judge. The news keeps getting worse for your Wilson woman. I'm one hundred percent against you continuing as her defense counsel. But more importantly, we need to talk about our son."

"Yes, Katy. Okay. Let's talk about Ralphie. What do you think we should we do?" Glad to change the subject. He was feeling over his head on this issue, and not just because his head hurt from too much red wine the night before. Katy was the high school counselor; this was her area of expertise, not his.

"Ralphie can't go back to The Strand Pre-School."

"Sadly, I think you're right, Katy. There's no pre-school to go back to. Between the Police Chief's letter and the arrest of Laura and Harry Wilson, I'm sure every parent has pulled their child out of the school. There's no revenue to pay the mortgage, the bank will shortly initiate foreclosure proceedings, and the Wilsons will lose everything."

"Serves them right for molesting small children."

"I don't believe any of it's true. Katy. But suppose… just suppose, there's some truth in this ugly rumor, do you think Ralphie might have been molested?"

The Judge immediately regretted his question, but it was too late. He just wasn't functioning on all cylinders this morning.

Katy's head swung around to look at the Judge with all the ferocity of a great white, her aqua eyes glaring. He instinctively stepped back.

"Now, I'm not saying he was, Katy." He put his hands in front of him, palms out. "Not saying that. I'm just asking questions. It's what lawyers do. Why don't we sit Ralphie down in his room this morning and we can ask him some questions?"

"You mean grill him?"

"Well…"

"He's barely five for Christ sakes, Judge. You can't treat this like one of your murder cases where we line Ralphie up against a wall and see if he'll spill his guts."

"No… No, I guess not."

"You come home early and we'll go for a drive this afternoon, Judge. Let's go down to the Del Amo Mall. On the drive over, in a very casual manner, I'll draw Ralphie out about his experiences at The Strand. And you, Judge, you just stay out of it, just drive, listen, and keep your trap shut."

"Alright, Katy. Alright."

Late in the afternoon they bundled Ralphie into the car and strapped him into his car seat under protest. He hated being tied down.

The little man was sporting designer jeans and a red-checked cowboy shirt, one of his favorites, clutching a prized stuffed dinosaur in one hand. The beast had apparently decided to accompany Ralphie on his trip.

"So Ralphie, how are you doing back there?" asked Katy, the very model of a relaxed mom conversing about nothing important with her son.

"'Kay."

"How do you like pre-school, honey?"

"Okay."

"You like Miss Laura."

"Uh-huh."

"You ever see Mr. Harry, the guy teacher?"

"Yeah."

"Does he play with you?"

"Sometimes."

"Does he ever play with you alone?"

"Huh?"

"Do you maybe go off sometimes just with Mr. Harry? Go somewhere else to play? By yourself?"

"Maybe sometimes."

"You like Mr. Harry?"

"Uh-huh."

"Did you know Mr. Harry and Miss Wilson are brother and sister?"

"Oh. She yells sometimes."

"Miss Laura?"

"Uh-huh."

"Miss Laura yells? She yells at you?"

"Uh-huh. Sometimes."

"What does she yell about?"

"Mark and I were in the boy's bathroom, playing spaceship. She came in and yelled at us to stop."

"Stop what?"

"Stop playing spaceship."

"How were you playing spaceship?" asked the Judge.

"You know dad. Flushing all the toilets at once and making them go *whishhhh*. They were our engines."

The Judge did know. He'd gotten in similar trouble when he'd been in kindergarten. It had earned him a trip to the principal's office. He smiled.

"Do you like to go to school there?" Katy asked.

"Uh-huh."

"You're happy there?"

"Uh-huh."

"Are you ever scared at the school?"

"Only when they yell at you."

"Did anyone ever take you out of class, besides Mr. Harry, honey?"

"Sure."

"Who?"

"The other teachers."

"Where do Mr. Harry and sometimes the other teachers take you?"

"Mostly to the bathroom."

"Do they come into the bathroom with you?"

"Sometimes. Sometimes I have to change my pants."

"Have the teachers taken you out of class for any other reason? Or taken you somewhere away from school?"

"I don't know. I don't remember."

"Have the teachers ever taken your temperature?"

"I don't know. What's that?"

"You know, dear. Sometimes you have a hot face or head, and I take your temperature. With a thermometer. I stick it in your mouth."

Ralphie giggled.

"What's so funny, Ralphie?" asked the Judge.

"Mark."

"Your friend, Mark?"

"Yeah." More giggling.

"Tell me dear," Katy said. "What happened with Mark?"

"Miss Wilson stuck it up his butt." Ralphie was giggling so hard he was rolling around in his car seat now.

"The thermometer?"

Ralphie nodded. "Mark said it tickled. But I wouldn't want it."

"Was Mark sick?"

"I guess so. He couldn't play anymore. He had to wait somewhere else until his mom came."

"He went off with Miss Wilson?"

"Uh-huh."

"Ralphie, did anyone ever tie you up?" asked the Judge.

Ralphie's eyes got big. "How'd you know about that, Dad?"

"I don't Ralphie. I was hoping you'd tell me."

"It's a game we play. Sometimes we're the cowboys and other kids are Indians, and we pretend to tie up the Indians. Sometimes we have to be the Indians and pretend to get tied up."

"Do you use real rope?"

"Naw, it's not allowed. But one-time Mark brought some cool string to school and we used that."

"It's a fun game?"

"Oh yeah."

"But no one really gets tied up?"

"No."

"Okay," said Katy. "Ralphie, have any of the teachers ever told you a secret?"

"Like what? I like secrets."

"I don't know, honey. That's why I'm asking."

"No… Maybe."

"Can you tell me the secret?"

"I'm not supposed to tell, Mom."

Katy shot the Judge a hard look.

"But you can tell me, honey, I'm your mom."

"I'm not supposed to."

"Perhaps you can tell me, Ralphie, and your mom won't listen," offered the Judge.

"Promise?"

"I promise," said Katy.

Ralphie pointed his lips toward the back of the Judge's head and said in a stage whisper, "I'm making Mom a surprise picture for her birthday. It's cool. I'm painting the frame. Sticking shells on. I have the picture to put in it too."

"That's really great, Ralphie," said the Judge. "Are there any other secrets at the school you're not supposed to talk about?"

"I don't know."

"Think about it a minute."

"Okay."

"Any other secrets?"

"No."

"We never got to play the movie star game, Ralphie," the Judge said.

"Oh yeah."

"And I don't know how to play. Can you tell me how you play?"

"Okay."

"Okay, Ralphie, go ahead. Tell me how you play that game."

"Right now?"

"Yes."

"Well, I don't know. I only played it once."

"How'd you play it that once?"

"We got in a group outside, by the big tree next door."

"The apple tree?"

"I think so. We got in a big circle and we danced around the tree, and we sang."

"What did you sing?"

"You know."

"I've forgotten. Can you sing if for me again?"

Ralphie gave a big sigh, then launched into song in his high tweedy voice.

"What you see... is what you are. You're a naked movie star! What I see is what you are. I'm a naked movie star! What we see is what we are, we're all naked movie stars!" This sent him into giggles.

"Were your teachers there when you went in the circle?"

"No. But they came over then. Said we had to come inside."

"Honey, did any of the teachers ever touch you?" Katy asked.

"Huh?"

"Maybe a teacher might have touched you in a private part?"

"What do you mean?"

"Did Mr. Harry, for instance, or Miss Wilson, ever touch you in a private part, maybe on your penis? Or on your butt?"

The Judge looked in the rear-view mirror at Ralphie, who looked worried now.

"Sometimes."

83

Katy's head swung around on an arc. Suddenly, she was nose to nose with her son in the back seat.

"Sometimes when?"

"Well, you know, sometimes."

"Like when? Why?"

"Mom... 'cause sometimes I need help."

"What do you need help for?

"When I go to the bathroom and do number two. When I have to change my pants sometimes."

"And who helps you?"

"Mostly Miss Laura."

"Anybody else?"

"Sometimes Miss Laura can't come, so Mr. Harry helps me."

"Only in the bathroom?"

"Uh-huh."

"Only when there's a problem?"

"Uh-huh."

"Ever outside?"

"Huh?"

"Did any of your teachers touch your private parts outside?"

"I don't know."

"Think about it, honey."

"Maybe."

"What happened?"

"I fell in some dirt. They helped me brush it off."

"Who?"

"Miss Laura."

"Did your teachers ever take pictures of you Ralphie?" asked the Judge.

"Uh-huh." He leaned a little in his car seat and whispered to the Judge. "For Mom's present."

"Did they ever take pictures while you were playing the movie star game?"

"I don't know."

"Did you ever play the movie star game and take your clothes off to play?"

"Dad…. No"

"Okay, okay, Ralphie, just asking."

Later, as Ralphie played in a small indoor playground in the mall, the Judge turned to Katy. "What do you think?"

"I don't know, Judge. I'm very nervous about this. I think we should talk to somebody."

"You and I?"

"No, Ralphie."

"Who?"

"The therapist recommended in that police letter."

"Oh, for crying out loud, Katy. Ralphie said nothing to indicate there was anything untoward going on."

"There's a damn lot at risk, Judge. Look at those poor unfortunate altar boys in the Catholic Church. They've carried their scars for years."

"Yeah, but this is different, Katy. Ralphie was only there a couple of weeks. And he said nothing to indicate there was any problem."

Katy's jaw tilted skyward. With Katy, always a bad sign. "I think our Ralphie should be checked out, Judge."

"But if nothing happened, going through a bunch of crap with a therapist may create damage where there is none."

"You don't know that, Judge. I say we play it safe. Go see the therapist."

"I don't see how going to be pawed over by some therapist is playing it safe."

"I know you have a bias against therapy, Judge. Ironic, here I am a high school counselor, and you don't believe in what I do. But this one is my call. We're going to have Ralphie checked out." Katy crossed her arms, signaling any further discussion would be futile.

The Judge sighed, exasperated. His bride was getting quite pig-headed. When it came to parenting it seemed he had no say at all.

"All right Katy. I think you're totally wrong about this. But I'll put aside my objections and distrust, so long as I can be there and observe what's going on and what the shrink is doing with Ralphie."

"We don't call them shrinks, Judge."

"Well that's too damn bad, 'cause that's what I call them." The Judge stomped away to get himself a Cinnabon and coffee, trying to control his frustration.

CHAPTER 15

The next morning the press was still fanning the flames of community outrage over The Strand Pre-School case. One paper reported therapeutic puppets, nude, with realistic genitals, used to elicit the children's sordid stories of forced pornography, rape, sodomy, oral copulation and fondling.

Some children said they'd played doctor games at The Strand with a physical exam and rectal thermometers. Others reported the slaughter of small animals in front of the them, with threats it would happen to them and their parents if the child ever spoke about it. Prosecutors reported they'd identified over three hundred children who'd been victimized at The Strand Pre-School.

"Thank you, prosecutors," mused the Judge. "Nothing like drilling deep in the jury pool to create a prejudice against the defendants before they ever reach trial."

The parents had joined in the South Bay communities to form a Me Too For Our Children movement called *Me Too Parents*. A website and an active blog were up, and organizers were pumping the community for further stories of molestation of children. According to the newspaper, the blog was jammed with responses.

The Judge had made an appointment to meet with Laura Wilson and Barney Malone at the holding jail downtown at ten. Glancing at his watch, he realized he had to get moving. He was going to be late given the miserable slog that was the Harbor Freeway into downtown Los Angeles at this hour.

The holding jail was ugly on the outside, light beige with six darker horizontal beige stripes defining each floor. It was all closed, no windows, like a stack of modern shoeboxes run amuck. It was depressing to look at from across the street, and even more depressing inside. Staffed by out of shape sheriffs and dispirited staff, tending to a variety of inmates, mostly poor, mostly minority, mostly disoriented, mostly depressed, many angry, some belligerent, and a few dangerous, boxed into their confined space.

The Judge felt like his soul being sucked out as he stepped into the lobby of the dreary place. He met Barney and huddled with him over paper cups of coffee from the little stand just inside the door, run by a wizen blind man who was the only jolly presence in the building. They had to wait for an interview room to become available upstairs, supposedly secure, private and not bugged. But you never knew. Orange County had just been called out for its recording of attorney client conversations over several years, a breach of the attorney-client privilege.

Barney suggested they settle in over better coffee across the street at the local coffee shop; it would be a while before a room opened up. They chose a table outside where they could talk discreetly.

Barney Malone was late forties. His short rotund figure, toothy grin, and friendly blue eyes gave him a youthful, almost boyish look. Irish Catholic and a committed family man, he was the wonder coach of his parish school's girls' softball team, coaching three daughters in successive years to state championships. And called back periodically by Our Lady of the Shepherd for advice when the current girls' softball team was in trouble.

Beneath his bland appearance lurked a legal mind constructed like a steel trap. He'd invariably jump right to the heart of a legal issue, and cleverly explain the simplicity of his client's position with sincerity to a jury that instantly liked him and wanted him to win. He was a dangerous combination of intellect and aw-shucks, making him a potent adversary in any courtroom and leaving a trail of anecdotes in his wake of pulling impossible chestnuts out of the fire for grateful clients.

He was a lawyer's lawyer, believing in the sacred oath all lawyers took to defend the law and extend its protections to all. As a younger lawyer he'd volunteered many pro bono hours to indigent causes, and now in mid-career, he was the first to donate his time and resources to functions organized to secure funding for the Law and Poverty Center and similar organizations. It was no doubt in part why he'd agreed to take Harry Wilson's case. That and the pure challenge of taking on Los Angeles County's politicking D.A.

"Let me fill you in on what I've learned so far, Judge."

"Go ahead."

"It's interesting that the Ocean Shore Chief of Police originally refused to make an arrest. Said he didn't think there was enough evidence for a collar."

The Judge nodded. "He told me as much."

"D.A. Nancy Aragon could taste the biggest case of her career, right when she needed it most, campaign-wise, but the intractable Police Chief with jurisdiction wouldn't arrest. So, Aragon did an end run."

"The grand jury."

"Right. She quickly convened a grand jury, sold them on her point of view, and got her indictment against Harry Wilson and Laura Wilson. The indictment alleges crimes of child abuse extending over the past four years.

Laura and Harry Wilson were arrested at their homes in the early evening after neighbors had returned from work and kids were back from school, at a time and in a manner calculated to provide maximum neighborhood consternation, disruption, and press coverage. The press was tipped off well ahead of time and there in full force with their cameras to record and broadcast the 'perp walk'. And the D.A. immediately called a press conference and popped around like a blue jay, pontificating about the case and about her record on crime. You probably saw it on TV."

"I did."

"Nearly three hundred children who attended The Strand were scheduled for interviews by Dr. Robert Gibson, a therapist and the Director at the Minor's Refuge for Change organization, or MRC. It's a non-profit specializing in child abuse therapy. But only about one-third of the kids have been interviewed thus far. Dr. Gibson has diagnosed forty-one of the kids interviewed as victims of child abuse, according to the complaint filed by the D.A."

"Jesus."

"As I said, the D.A. was in a hurry to get the warrants issued and the case started, given her upcoming election. You'd normally interview everyone before you file. Search warrants have been served at eleven locations across three counties, looking for print, video and computer evidence of child pornography. My sources tell me so far those searches have come up dry. But now the FBI has joined the fray, looking for the sale of photos of nude children from The Strand. And the Sheriff's crime lab people are examining a vacant lot next door, where some children say there are secret tunnels and they watched animals killed and buried. Killed to scare them into silence."

"Have they found anything in the lot?"

"My source says so far just a single tortoise shell and the old bones of couple of gophers. No underground passages. Nothing very dramatic."

"How has the D.A. charged in the case, Barney?"

"She's charged Laura Wilson with fifteen counts, alleging oral copulation, fondling, and penetration with a foreign object."

"No way."

"Way. She's charged Harry Wilson with seventy-five counts of molestation, oral copulation, fondling and penetration with a foreign object. That's as much as I know right now."

"You've seen the press coverage in the papers and on TV and radio, Barney? The press is whipping people into a fine hysteria."

"How could I miss it? The D.A. is fanning the flames, basking in the fiery glow, and spouting off about her tough record on crime. It's like the entire criminal justice system and the press have forgotten our basic tenant under the Constitution: *'Innocent until proven guilty'.*"

CHAPTER 16

Laura filled out her light prison suit fetchingly, tall, broad-shouldered, well stacked, proportionate hips, a flat stomach, fire-red hair clashing with the blue of her outfit. But her face was a mess, dark circles under her eyes, eyelids red from tears and a sleepless night, her hair in scattered condition, not piled on her head in the latest fashion as the Judge had seen her last. Her lipstick and mascara were missing, no earrings or jewelry. Her lips were a thin line of bitterness. She'd dramatically aged. She was a wreck.

Laura rose from her chair to offer the Judge a limp handshake, staring into his eyes with a panicky question easy to read: could he get her out of this? He wasn't sure, but he had to project confidence for them both.

Harry, her brother, looked equally bad. Little sleep, bad food and huge stress will do that.

They both shook hands with Barney in the same tired way, then slumped back into their chairs while the Judge explained that he would represent Laura and Barney would represent Harry. They'd put on a coordinated defense.

"So," the Judge said, addressing Laura and Harry, "tell Barney about the history of The Strand Pre-School, how you've operated, why it's a closed campus in the middle of the day, any parent complaints you've had, and anything else you believe to be relevant. Whatever you say is privileged."

Laura and Harry waded in, taking turns telling of their operation of the pre-school and their relationships with the children and the parents.

"Better describe what happened the morning you found the body of Jeffrey Simpson in your maintenance room. In fact, tell us all about Jeffrey, how he became an employee of the school, what he did, what his hours were, what you paid him."

"I hired him," said Laura. "Six months ago, as our maintenance man. I'd posted a job opening online and he applied for it. He seemed qualified and enthusiastic and was a vet. I like to hire vets. He was to be at the school and on call on an eight to five shift daily during the week, with an hour off for lunch. Mr. Simpson was hired to do maintenance and repairs, gardening, trash removal, run errands and generally be available during our hours of operation to help out. His office was the maintenance room, and he was welcome to stay there overnight as a secondary home, or maybe primary, I don't know. Anyway, there was a cot, and he was welcome to sleep over."

"And how did he do at the job?" asked the Judge.

"Initially great. But lately he'd been tardy showing up. A couple of times he left early without telling anyone. One week he failed to cut the lawn. I gave him a punch list of simple repairs a few weeks back, and it seemed like it took forever for him to get anything done."

"Did you speak to him about it?"

"Several times, but things weren't improving. If anything, they were getting worse. Harry and I finally decided we had to let him go. His termination date was to be the day after the date he killed himself."

"How'd he take it?"

"Not well. He got very angry, stomped around the maintenance room, called me a 'bitch'. When that happened, I just turned and left. I didn't need to deal with that crap."

"Did you know he was going to meet with the Ocean Hill Police, allegedly about the child molestation allegations?"

"No."

"Okay, Laura, is there anything else I should know about this guy, or what happened?

"No."

"You're sure? Absolutely nothing else about this guy, Jeffrey Simpson? Relevant or not?"

"No."

"Harry, you have anything to add?"

"No. Laura summed it up pretty well."

"Barney?"

"I'm good."

Barney then waded into the details of his rates, retainer, cheerful payment plan, security (Harry's house would be pledged to secure payment of legal fees), the scope of his work, what would happen if there was a retrial, or an appeal from an adverse verdict, and so on.

He finished by fishing a retainer agreement out of his briefcase and flapping it across the small desk to Harry, offering a pen to sign it. Harry took the agreement, running to five pages, and slowly read through, sliding further down in his chair as he read, contemplating the financial ruin his defense would entail.

"What about a public defender for me, Judge?" asked Harry. "I haven't done anything wrong."

"You certainly have the right to one, Harry. But your freedom's at stake. You have the assets. I wouldn't risk a public defender in your shoes. The D.A. will go after you tooth and tong with everything she can think of. She needs a big win on a high priority case to help her re-election campaign. She's not going to consider what's fair, only whether she can sell a jury and obtain a conviction."

"Is she going to try the case for the prosecution?"

"Nancy Aragon, no. But I hear she's going to use her best prosecutor, an attorney by the name of Jay Armstrong. Barney and I know him well. He's smart, charismatic, and tough, almost to the point of ruthlessness, in his quest for convictions."

Harry sighed.

"But Barney will do a good job," the Judge continued. "He's clever and experienced; just look at him."

Barney beamed. He did love praise.

"And Barney's rates are fair. He's my best choice for you, Harry."

Laura looked at the Judge, spreading her hands, indicating she didn't own a house to pledge to secure the Judge's fees. The Judge produced his own fee agreement. It provided for no retainer up front. "Don't worry about your fees, Laura." The Judge said. "We'll figure it out later."

Laura gave him a wan smile and mouthed a 'thank you'.

"It's just so sad, Judge," said Harry. "The Strand Pre-School is lost. The school's reputation is being trashed in the press. All the kids have been pulled out of the school and it has closed. The school will never come back. Now we're going to lose our savings too, and my house. We've worked and saved so hard, and now... well... you know... these false charges are sweeping away all that we've accumulated and all we've worked for. It's just suddenly gone. It's so... hard."

Laura nodded her head in agreement. She turned to the last page of the Judge's fee letter and scribbled a signature, not bothering to read it. Then she began to cry softly.

They waited awhile, silently, the three men, looking uncomfortable as men do when a female cries, until finally Laura regained some composure, using the back of her hands to brush moisture from her cheeks and eyes.

"Alright gentlemen," she finally whispered, trying to hold her head high. "What's next?"

CHAPTER 17

"There are said to be secret underground tunnels at the school where the Satanic cult operates, holding ceremonies with the children which involved the torture and death of small animals, nude games, nude photographs, sexual touching, and so on. Sources report of killing rabbits, mutilating of small animal corpses, and drinking of blood in a makeshift Devil's church."

The morning news anchorman continued to whine on. The Judge had set the timer on his TV to turn the set on as an alarm to get up. He was awake now for sure. The TV display said 8:03 a.m.

He glanced at Katy, a covered lump under the sheets beside him, blond mane poking out, eyes hidden under one arm, protected from the light streaming in like honey from their large window. They needed blackout drapes, but then, of course, the over-sleeping would be worse. He might never get up.

Later in the morning, the Judge arrived in the courtroom seconds before his case was to be called. But then the clerk announced that Judge Ferguson wasn't ready and there'd be a fifteen-minute delay.

The Judge took a seat at the defense table, Laura to his right and Barney to his left so the two attorneys could confer, with Harry on the other side of Barney.

The District Attorney's second in command, Deputy District Attorney In charge, Jay Armstrong, sat at the prosecution's table. Next to him was a young blonde attorney, a pretty thing, mid-twenties, blue eyes, pink cheeks, dark blue pantsuit, with pants stretched across a rump on display as she bent over the bottom drawer of the biggest rolling file the Judge had ever seen in court. It was a full ten drawers high, higher than the young lawyer, metal, powder-coated in a soft avocado. It must have taken three bailiffs to wheel the thing up the elevator and into the courtroom. She was bending over the bottom drawer, stuffed with documents, nervously checking for likely the tenth time that the file tabs were +all in order. Symptomatic of a 'just minted' member of the State Bar on her first trial.

The Judge looked at their defense table. They didn't have a fancy rolling file, or even a box. Flat beside him on the table was a vintage brown leather courier case, double strapped, creased and double creased and even cracked here and there, the scars of long wear and affection. It didn't look like it contained much; no smartly tabbed files.

It was always the case when a private lawyer representing an individual came up against the government. Unless your client was super rich, you couldn't match the vast resources the government fielded against you in matters of investigation, laboratory analysis, depth of lawyers and investigators, and expert witnesses. It would be an uphill fight.

Barney turned to the Judge, and whispered, "You're looking dapper this morning, Judge."

"That's because I'm only half awake, Barney. How are we doing? What's the story on bail? Can we get them released on their own recognizance, or with a reasonable bail? "

"Normally I'd say yes, Judge. But the prosecution has asked that the defendants be held without bail."

"But that's not right," snapped Harry, eavesdropping from his end of the table. "Can they do that? This isn't a capital case."

"They've done it," Barney answered, "or at least made the motion to do it. California law allows a judge to deny bail where the defendant is charged with a felony involving violence or sexual assault, if there's strong evidence of guilt and a substantial likelihood that the defendant would cause substantial bodily harm to another if released."

"But we're innocent," said Harry.

"So we say. But the standard for holding someone without bail is flexible. It is not necessary that the evidence be so convincing as to justify guilt. It is sufficient if the evidence points to the defendant and induces the belief in the presiding judge that the defendant may have committed the crime."

"Where's the evidence like that?"

"We'll see. The D.A.'s office is pushing hard for no bail, building off the notoriety in the press, which has essentially tried and convicted you two already. The D.A. is going to milk this case for all it's worth. And it doesn't help that our presiding judge is up for re-election himself. In a high-profile case like this neither the D.A. nor the judge can afford to look soft on crime."

"Shit."

They were interrupted by the clerk, calling them to all rise so they could watch Judge Ferguson stroll in and take his position on the raised dais, swishing his robe as he walked like some giant black moth. The Judge surveyed the paneled courtroom with its matching wood seats and rails, no windows, raised platform, ceremonial outfits for the presiding judge and bailiff, the bailiff at high attention with the gun on his hip and a shiny badge. It was all high theater for masses, lending credence and pomp to something as old as time, one member of the community judging another. With a thud of the gavel Ferguson indicated the proceeding was to begin.

Armstrong got up to speak first. Jay Armstrong was a tall lanky guy, perhaps six foot four, white, mid-fifties. His head was clean shaven, preferring the Yul Brynner look to puffy side patches on his balding head. Hard, penetrating dark eyes focused on you with the intensity of a Texas Bobcat, almost as steely in their glitter as the shiny metal glasses they looked through. He was smart, agile, tough, experienced. Barney and the Judge were in for a serious fight.

The faint whiff of a Texas accent punctuated Armstrong's speech now and then as he rattled off his arguments like a Gatling gun, launching into a long harangue on how awful the defendants were, the sordid things they'd done to so many small children who were young and helpless and unable to defend themselves, how the witnesses were frightened for their safety, why there was no question but that defendants must remain incarcerated before trail. In other words, no bail. By the time Armstrong finished, the Judge could taste the tension in courtroom as all eyes turned to stare at the defendants and their defense counsel.

One witness was produced by Armstrong, a parent, who testified that both she and her child, and she believed many of the other children, were terrified of the defendants. Fearful the Wilsons would be turned back onto the street, free to intimidate and even attack their accusers; if freed, who knew what these monsters might do.

Barney got up next, cutting a somewhat rumpled figure in his wrinkled suit, starched white shirt, and ugly bowtie, no doubt picked out by one of his young daughters and worn with pride regardless. Barney Malone stood five-foot-six and risked being lost in the shadow of Jay Armstrong. He looked up at Ferguson with his soft rounded face, punctuated by a toothy smile, and his most amazingly clear blue eyes.

The Judge Ferguson sat back in his chair and relaxed, as did everybody else in the room; Barney was that kind of guy. People just naturally liked Barney. The Judge knew that behind that folksy exterior lay a foxy legal mind, smart, tenacious, and ready to pounce on any misstep by the prosecution.

Barney objected to the parent's testimony as hearsay, which most of it was, and also argued there was absolutely no concrete evidence of any wrongdoing by the defendants. The Judge got up next to make his argument.

"The State hasn't produced a single witness to testify there's even a crime been committed, your honor. If the State truly has one or more child witnesses, put one or two on the stand and let's hear from them. The second and third-hand testimony of this parent, who admits she was not present at any alleged molestation and has no testimony to give us of a crime committed based on her own physical observation, is neither admissible nor relevant in this hearing to set bail."

But Ferguson was not buying it. After further argument from both sides, he brought his gavel down to cut off further discussion, finding that the defendants posed a danger to public safety and were to be held without bail.

CHAPTER 18

After the hearing, Barney and the Judge settled in over lunch at the Pacific Dining Car, the local joint attorneys liked after a sweaty and anxiety-ridden morning spent in court. Particularly if they'd won, as the Dining Car was expensive. Founded in 1921 and wrapped inside realistic railroad dining cars just a mite wider than real ones, The Pacific Dining Car at Sixth and Wilmer had flourished in L.A. through the Roaring Twenties, the desperate Thirties, World War II, and the onslaught of baby-boomers, ownership of the business handed down from generation to generation. It served the best steaks to be had in L.A.

"What do you think, Judge? Off the record. Just between us. Did Laura Wilson and her brother do any of this? Were they running a sex ring at The Strand?"

"I can't believe it, Barney. I've known Laura Wilson for years. She'd never get involved with anything like that."

"In my business you learn quickly you never really know anyone, Judge, and that goes double for women."

"But Laura? Come on…"

"How close were you to Laura, Judge? And don't try to kid a kidder."

The Judge sighed. "We were an item once upon a time Barney. Long before I met Katy. Katy doesn't need to know the details. And neither do you."

"Wow, you really get around Judge."

The Judge could feel color coming into his face like the heat of a sunburn, beginning at his neck, marching upward.

"You were intimate?" Barney continued.

"A gentleman never tells."

"Come on, Judge. The lady's freedom is at stake. I want to hear anything and everything you can tell me about her."

"Yes. We were lovers"

"Well?"

"You want details?"

"Damn right I do."

The Judge sighed again.

"Did she like kinky sex, Judge? Windward passage stuff. Bindings? Playing with a third wheel or another couple? S&M stuff?"

"No. No, none of that. It was just the usual fun and games. Nothing kinky. Just normal stuff."

"Was she exclusive?"

"Sure. I mean I think so. Hell, I don't know. I didn't ask. It wasn't that serious."

"Were you?"

"Hey. I'm not the one on trial here."

"Did she ever have any risqué photographs of herself?"

"Not that I saw."

"Of you? Of young children? Of anyone?"

"Hell, she was a firefighter. She was living a boy scout sort of existence, one week on, one week off, with a bunch of firemen. She wouldn't have had anything like that."

"You never saw any pictures of young people? On her computer? At her place?"

"No, she was perfectly normal. Or mostly so."

"How not so?"

"Well…"

"Come on, Judge. Spill it."

"She did have an enormous appetite for sex. Hell, none of this is relevant. Like I said in our earlier conversation, you're just a dirty old man."

Barney smiled, putting a hand on the Judge's arm. "Okay, Okay, Judge. Relax. You're very comical when you get aroused."

The Judge snorted.

Barney leaned back in his seat. "I suggest we divide up our work on this case. Since criminal law is my specialty, I'll focus on the legal research and the motion work."

"So where should I spend my time?"

"I've been talking to some friends at the D.A.'s office, Judge, off the record. I'm even more concerned for our clients because our politicking D.A., Nancy Aragon, really wants to make this a murder case."

"Jeffrey Simpson?"

"Yes. The D.A. and the police don't have an autopsy report yet, but they strongly suspect this was a homicide, not a suicide. They'd love to pin the homicide on Laura, and maybe Harry too. They're running with the idea that Simpson had a date the next day at the police station to spill his guts about the sex ring at the school, tie their case up neat and tight. He was murdered to stop him from talking."

"That's baloney."

"That may be, but that's what they think."

"We don't even know it's murder, Barney. It looks like a suicide. Besides, how could Laura lift Simpson up and hang him from a beam?"

"She's a firefighter, isn't she? That's what they do, for Christ sake. And Simpson is a small guy. Besides, maybe Harry helped her."

"It's absurd."

"Maybe, Judge, maybe not. The police are out there now trying to check the boxes to prove it wasn't suicide. To show that Laura Wilson murdered Jeffrey Simpson. You know how they work. They get an idea someone's involved. Then they go around looking for facts, or pseudo-facts, to support their theory."

"Yes, and ignore other possible perps in the process."

"So, I'm thinking, Judge, that the best use of your time when we're not in court is to find out if Simpson took his own life, or not. And if it was a homicide, we need you to find who 'done it'. You've got something of a reputation as a detective, and boy do we need those skills now. You nose around and find out what really happened. We don't want to end up with a couple of clients that fry."

CHAPTER 19

The TV alarm awoke the Judge the next morning to the gravelly voice of a veteran newscaster who fancied himself an investigative reporter. He shoved a report in front of the camera, filling the TV screen at the Judge's end, blotting out the studio and any light that might have made the report legible on the screen.

"This police report says Harry Wilson has been counseled by the chaplain of his own church for sexual problems involving children. If this isn't a smoking gun, I don't know what is. And the perps have lawyered up with an ex-judge, thrown off the bench by the people of this state for his liberal tendencies. Now a person of interest in the investigation."

A picture of the Judge appeared on the screen taken some years before, along with his full legal name.

"The bastards!" muttered the Judge.

The Judge rolled the pillow on top of his head, trying to drown out the sunlight and the voice of the newscaster. It worked for neither. Finally, resigned, he rolled out of the bed and headed to the bathroom for a whizz, noting Katy was already gone, switching the TV to another news channel as he passed. The story was on there too, with an anchorman beating his chest about what might have happened had bail been granted and the Wilsons allowed back on the street. The tribe was sharpening its collective knives.

The Judge went into his study and looked at the list of people connected to Jeffrey Simpson. He'd gotten the names from Laura. She seemed to know quite a bit about her former maintenance man.

There was a brother, an ex-wife now shacked up with some new boyfriend, a mother, a girlfriend of the moment, two surfer buddies, an army buddy, and a doctor at the VA who Jeffrey had been seeing twice a month.

The Judge sighed. There was no easy way. If he wanted to discover what happened in that maintenance room, he needed to talk to these people. The brother was at the top of Laura's list; it was where Jeffrey had been sleeping when he didn't stay over in the maintenance room. The Judge would start there. Perhaps he could combine some exercise with his investigation.

The Judge went to his closet and after pawing around at the back, came up with stretchy bicycle pants in a tomato red with black trim, and a matching red top. Katy had bought the outfit a year before for the Judge on her own, when he'd said he would join a bicycle club for exercise. But his talk about the bike club, all the exercise he'd get and so on, turned out just to be talk once he heard the length of their weekend rides. He hadn't joined. But he still had the outfit and he'd even bought a bike.

He pulled the pants on over his feet, up his legs, and with some difficulty, up over his paunch. Then he wiggled into the top. The outfit was surprisingly tight. Must have shrunk from hanging in the closet. He turned sideways to admire himself in the mirror.

It wasn't the Red Hornet he saw reflected. He looked like a tomato, perhaps a pregnant tomato from the side view, what with his paunch and large fanny. Too many years just sitting. This was the final straw; he'd give up ice cream for the coming week.

When his bicycle club resolve evaporated, the Judge had traded his new club bike in for something more practical, an electric bike. The Judge tried a demo on a few electric bikes with Katy, but he always bitched and moaned about the fact he still had to pedal the pedals, and on hills to pedal hard. Some people actually thought you were supposed to pedal on an electric bike. What a stupid idea. He was looking for exercise, not exertion.

The Judge marched to the garage, threw off the old sheet cover, and unplugged his new electric bike from its charger, wheeling it out on to his driveway. It was a A2B Monster High Performance Bike, souped up with a 72-volt battery which gave it sustained speeds of over sixty miles per hour. But key was the ability of all that power to boost the Judge's 225 pounds up a damn steep hill without pedaling. He just sat on the seat and steered. The machine whizzed by other bicycles and right up the steepest hills, leaving a trail of exhausted and envious bikers behind gasping for air, making him feel smug at the miles he was churning off and the exercise he was gaining.

He stuck the foolish looking bike helmet on, and with difficulty buckled the strap under his chubby chin, impairing his vision but making him legally compliant. The damn thing looked like a spider on his head, slowly devouring him with its tentacle straps. Why were bike helmets always too small?

He coasted down his driveway, down Via Del Monte, the twisting road that swooped its way back and forth across Malaga Cove from his house to the Malaga Cove Plaza, and then shot out onto Palos Verdes Boulevard, dodging cars and a chorus of horns and middle fingers. PV drivers were a bit snotty, thinking they owned the road, hating bicyclists. He used to think that way too, until he got his bike. Ah, perspective.

He cranked the bike up to fourth gear, felt the wind in his hair, a slight wobble in the bike, and thought perhaps he did look like the Red Hornet tearing along. It was exhilarating.

He turned left on Via Rivera, and coasted down to its end, and then down the driveway there to RAT Beach, short for Redondo And Torrance State Beach, and swung to a stop at the start of The Strand Bike Path. The Strand was what everyone called the concrete ribbon of bike path running north along the beach, all the way to the edge of Marina Del Rey. He swung onto the path, keeping the bike speed low, to a soft purr. He hoped no one noticed the big battery or speculated that the bike might go faster than the posted twenty miles per hour, the maximum speed a bike was allowed to be capable of traveling and still be legal on The Strand bike path.

It was still early and the path was reasonably empty at its RAT Beach tip, but quickly picked up traffic as he sped along through Redondo, Hermosa, and then into Ocean Hill. He found himself blocked at various times by bike clubs, all sporting their gaudy colored jerseys, and looking askance as he perched on his seat, feet resting comfortably on stationary pedals, whizzing in, out and around, roaring past. It was all very satisfying.

The Judge pulled over at Twelfth Street, three blocks north of The Strand Pre-School's street. He pulled out his cell and punched in the address of Jeffrey's brother, whose place was beachfront further along The Strand. It was another six blocks.

He started off again, admiring the surf curling up on the sand to his left, and the mostly glitzy houses sliding by on his right, filled with the L.A. rich. Doctors, lawyers, investment bankers, divorced businessmen who'd left their families in Brentwood and Belair and come here for a new life and a piece of the action. The Strand was filled now with bikers, pedestrians, and roller skaters. Many were young and not so young women in skimpy shorts and tops, mostly in clusters of twos and threes, trolling the sidewalks, hoping to meet a male with a nest on The Strand. And the homeless were here too, ubiquitous in L.A., downtrodden people pushing carts or carrying bags with their few possessions, a sad commentary on a society so rich in material things, so poor in spirit. It was easier for people to look away than to try to alleviate some of the poverty for those at the bottom.

He braked in front of a small ancient cottage squeezed between two modern wood and glass two-stories, all gleam and polished metal. Its small patio was enclosed in a three-foot-high grey cinderblock wall, stained and cracked here and there.

A man was on the lounge on the patio, prone on his back, face to the sun. He looked to be mid-forties, short blond stubble around his ears framing a balding pate. He wore red trunks which offset his deep tan, but his tan didn't extend around his eyes. He must mostly wear sunglasses, leaving two white circles of flesh and lines. It gave him a racoon look.

The Judge brought the bike to a stop and hopped off, leaning the bike against the wall, calling over, "Nice day."

Racoon Eyes sat up, eyes narrowing as he assessed the Judge. "You a reporter?"

"No. You Erwin Simpson, Jeff's brother?"

"Yeah. Police?"

"No. Defense attorney for Laura Wilson."

"She do it? She kill my little brother?" Racoon's voice rose an octave.

"She says no. Besides, it looks to be suicide. The police are nosing around, but I've seen no evidence that would implicate her in his death. You don't think Jeffrey took his own life?"

Racoon's eyes were cold now. "Anything's possible, but I saw no signs of it. I think they may have killed my baby brother for what he knew. What he could tell the police about what went on at The Strand Pre-School. The bastards. I hope they send them away forever."

"Who?"

"The Wilsons."

He stood up then, abandoning his chaise lounge, walking over to his side of the wall to give the Judge a closer look. "That's kind of an interesting outfit you have on. Are you in a bike club or something?"

"Used to be," lied the Judge. "You like it? It's easy to see in the dark."

"I'll bet," said Racoon Eyes. "Be hard to miss."

"Can I come in?" the Judge asked. "Can we talk a little about your brother?"

"Why? Why would I want to talk to you, Mr. Fancy-Pants defense lawyer? I don't have to talk to you. You can go suck wind."

"Wouldn't you like to know?"

"Know what?"

"Whether it was suicide?"

Erwin Simpson considered a minute.

"Yeah. I suppose. But I've not got much to say. Jeffrey's dead. Talk won't bring him back."

The Judge walked to where a faded blue wooden gate, low, like the wall, provided access, and let himself into the patio.

"Just talk to me for a minute. Maybe between us we can figure out what happened to your brother. It's worth a shot."

"I don't know. It's like fraternizing with the enemy."

"It's really not." The Judge gave his given name. "But they call me the Judge. It's in both our interests to find out why and how Jeffrey died, suicide or otherwise. Just tell me a little about Jeffrey. What kind of brother was he?"

Erwin considered for a long moment. Then, "He was my baby brother. He was a sweet kid. I'm angry this happened… that he's gone. It's not right. Not fair."

"Was he having difficulties?"

"Listen, we all have difficulties. Life's no bed of roses all the time for anyone. Sure. Jeffrey had some issues. He had a pretty traumatic time in Afghanistan. He was never the same after."

"PTSD."

"That's sort of a loose name they apply to everybody who nearly got killed over there serving our country and now has issues. Sure, call it that. But life was mostly always difficult for Jeffrey."

"How so?"

"Jeff was a needy guy. Needed to escape a lot. Found it difficult to focus for long periods. Was jumpy, quick to anger, couldn't stand supervision. And you couldn't rely on Jeffrey to do stuff. You could give him a task, or an assignment, but then he'd just fade off into something else, let you down, never get the job done. Life was just more difficult for him than for the rest of us."

"Did he escape into alcohol? Drugs?"

"I suppose a bit. Can't blame him after what he went through. Who wouldn't? Doesn't mean he killed himself."

"Jeffrey lived here? With you?"

"Yeah, kind of, last six months. He was broke. Till he got the job with that Strand Pre-School. Then he was still broke. No savings. The school didn't pay much. Told him he could use my extra bedroom whenever he needed. I even gave him a little work to do. But he let me down, as he always did. I had to find some other people to fill in for him."

"What kind of work?"

"Just stuff with my film production company, nothing important."

"So, he was here a lot."

"Actually, he wasn't. Not much. Either working, or surfing, or partying I guess, don't know. He slept here some nights when I first gave him the key. Then after he got the job at The Strand, he kind of just disappeared. I haven't seen him for some weeks, and now this."

"Can I see his room?"

"I don't have to show you that." Erwin's jaw set. Clamming up.

"No. You don't. But I'm just trying to find out what really happened. You said you'd like to know."

Erwin frowned, then his face relaxed, resigned.

"Okay. Come on. You can look. The police have been here already, didn't find anything, but you can look too. His digs are back here."

Erwin led the Judge in through the sliding-glass doors into the living room. Ancient shag carpet in a green hue competed with beige walls recently painted. One wall had three framed movie posters, each listing Erwin Simpson as the Producer: 'Kiss of the Camel Woman', 'Hard in Harlem' and 'The Summer Bitch', movies the Judge had never heard of and from the look of the posters, didn't want to.

Erwin led the Judge across the living room and down a narrow corridor to the back of the house, opening the last door on the left. It was a modest room with a single bed, neatly made, things stored away, no clutter. One wall was entirely taken with an old Channel Islands surf board in bright yellow with black markings, heavily waxed and looking ready to lift off the wall and go. Off the bedroom was a small bathroom with a toilet and minuscule shower.

The Judge turned back to the bedroom. Someone had thrown a small stack of mail on the bed.

"Is that new mail for Jeff?" asked the Judge.

"Just came in last night. Threw it there. Not quite sure what to do with it."

"Can I look at it?"

"Sure. Guess Jeff won't be paying these bills. Have to be an estate or something."

The Judge picked up the mail and sorted through. A cell phone bill, a renewal subscription to a surfer magazine, and a flyer from a local realtor touting a listing for a nearby condo for two million bucks. Housing prices had gone crazy in Los Angeles.

"Can I open the phone bill?"

"Go ahead."

The Judge took the bill out of its envelope, using his forefinger to split the top, and spread it out. There were over one hundred and fifty calls for the month. One caught the Judge's eye. He recognized the number, a six-p.m. call to the Ocean Hill Police Department the evening before Jeffrey died.

"I'd like to make a copy of this and then send it back to you if I might. Would you mind?"

"Not if it helps explain what happened. Just return it quickly so there're no late fees. My suspicion is I'm going to end up paying it."

"Jeff have a girlfriend?"

"Several. Guess sex helped too."

"Anyone special?"

"There was one. More friend than girlfriend, but they used to have at it a lot. Kept me awake some nights. She was a noisy broad. Guess I was a little envious."

"You married?"

"Divorced. Like everyone in this town."

"This gal wasn't too serious?"

"Wanted a no-strings-attached relationship, is what Jeff told me."

"What was her name?"

"Clair. Clair Henderson."

"Was there anyone else?"

"There was someone he was totally involved with recently. Really hurt Jeff when she dumped him. Turned out to be a flash in the pan for a couple of months for her. But Jeff thought they were in love, they were going to live together in a house with a white picket fence, or something. You can't ever trust females, particularly the L.A. variety."

"You know why she dumped him?"

"He told me. But it's kind of personal."

"He's gone now, Erwin. He won't mind."

Erwin shrugged.

"Jeff told me after Afghanistan his plumbing didn't always work so well. As he got more emotionally attached to this gal, it started to fail a lot. She got disappointed, so she just cut him off. A cold bitch."

"Do you know her name?"

"No. He never said. It was big secret for some reason, but I think they had a little love nest somewhere. As I said, he wasn't sleeping here much."

"When did it end?"

"Not sure, but very recently. Jeff was moping around about it last I saw him."

"So, Jeff was depressed?"

"Wouldn't you be? Sure, he was depressed."

"Depressed enough to kill himself?"

"I don't think so. It was a bad time for him, what with being dumped by her, and then losing Frosty, but Jeffrey would never kill himself. He just wouldn't."

"Frosty? Who's Frosty?"

"The beat-up old dog he had. A golden and poodle mix. He loved that dog."

"It died?"

"Yeah. Some asshole on a motorcycle ran the dog down. My brother didn't have time to do anything but watch it happen."

The Judge flashed on a street leading down to the beach in North Ocean Hill, a small young man in the middle of the street, holding a crumpled creature, a dog, in his arms, sobbing. Of course. That's where he'd seen Jeffrey Simpson before. The young man with the broken dog.

"They ever catch the guy?"

"Naw. Police didn't give a shit. To them it was just a dog. To Jeff that was his whole life, his baby, slept with Frosty in his bed when he didn't have company, fed Frosty from the table, talked to Frosty all the time, like the dog could understand."

"So, whoever hit the dog, it was just a random accident?"

"I'm sure it was, hit and run. But Jeff was real upset."

"Maybe that… the loss of Frosty, pushed him over the edge."

"It's hard to believe anyone would kill themselves over a dog. But then again, Frosty was practically Jeff's last friend in the world… Shit, I don't know."

"Any friends of Jeff's you know about?"

"Couple I guess. There was two surfer guys I met, …Matt something… Matt Singer. And there was Hank Tanaka. Both surfing buddies."

"Here in Ocean Hill?"

"Nearby. One in Hermosa and one in RAT Beach. There was also an army buddy I met once, bumped into Jeff and him on The Strand on my bike and Jeff introduced me."

"Name?"

"Sam something. Sam Richards… Sam Reynolds… Sam something like that. I think they met at the VA."

"Jeff was going to the VA?"

"Yeah, twice a month, counseling for his PTSD."

"Who was he seeing there?"

"Haven't a clue."

"Who were the other people in his life, Erwin?"

"That was about it. Our mom of course. Jeff's ex-wife, Louisa, truly a bitch… and her asshole boyfriend. They gave Jeff a lot of shit."

The Judge thanked Erwin for his time and headed back through the house and out the patio to his bike. Erwin followed him, watching from the patio door with his sad racoon eyes.

CHAPTER 20

The Judge was in his Venice office struggling with the exact legal language for a license agreement he was preparing for a client, when his cell rang.

"Damn, Judge, I'm glad I got you."

"Barney?"

"Yes. I need your help. I'm tied up at the courthouse on another matter, and our grand-standing D.A. has decided to give a press conference on The Strand Pre-School. I can't make it but I'm hoping you can. And where do you think Nancy's holding it?"

"At the D.A.'s office?"

"No."

"On the courthouse steps?"

"No."

"In front of the Times building?"

"Closer. She's holding it in front of the Ocean Hill Pier."

"To drum up support for her re-election campaign."

"You've got it. In about forty-five minutes. Can you make it?"

"Yes. I'll head over in five. It's much closer from here."

"Great. Let me know what the windbag has to say."

The Judge closed his computer, threw some work in his briefcase, and headed for the door. It was unusual for the District Attorney to go all the way out to Ocean Hill to hold a news conference on the beach.

The Judge found parking on 11th Avenue and walked down toward the beach and onto The Strand, dodging a jumble of bodies with lots of skin showing, walking, jogging, rollerblading, bicycling, or just leaning against the barrier wall that divided the sand. To his left, a fierce game of volleyball was underway, played by two all-girl teams in tight two-piece swimsuits. A clutch of young men, college age and older, clustered low on the sand to one side, ogling the teams.

A variety of umbrellas dotted the sand here and there in vivid colors, looking like overripe mushrooms gone wrong, sheltering kids and parents, most oily with sunscreen, the parents inscrutable behind sunglasses. It was a warm day and it was The Strand. The beautiful people, and the not so beautiful, were all out strutting their stuff.

A block up the bike path the Judge could see a crush of humanity where reporters streamed in like birds of prey, circling around a small platform with a tired wooden podium set up just off the bikeway on the street. The Judge joined the small clutch of news people setting up tripod cameras and opening flip books, pens at the ready. Soon a black limo pulled carefully down Ocean Hill Boulevard to the Pier, stopped, and D.A. Nancy Aragon got out. Her appearance sent a bolt of energy through the gathered throng which now numbered perhaps thirty.

Aragon looked every bit the crusading district attorney, black pantsuit and an expensive white starched shirt with soft collar. She was a tall woman, mid-fifties like the Judge, just under six foot, heavyset, carefully disguised by the cut of her clothes. She had dark snapping eyes, set a little too close together for the Judge's taste, and short dark hair, pulled back in a severe bun. Nancy wasted no time, diving into her prepared speech, presenting the image of a woman with other very important things to do.

"I'm here to report we have filed additional charges of child molestation which occurred in the community of Ocean Hill. These charges cover two hundred and eight instances of sexual abuse involving forty-two children. We have also identified an additional thirty individuals who have been placed under investigation, and no, I won't give you their names right now."

The Judge wondered if he had been placed under investigation, given his run-in at The Strand with the Ocean Hill Detective and his unpleasant conversation with that asshole reporter, Bradford Jones.

"We know the pornographic photographs and videos are out there, and we know for a fact that these children were abused. We are going to find their pornography. We have the ringleaders under lock and key. We're going to be putting these people away for a very long time."

There followed a barrage of questions, but Nancy either repeated the information she'd already given, or declined to answer. Nothing else of relevance got said.

Bringing the press conference to a close, Nancy reminded the reporters, "Despite what my opponent says, I'm the one in this race who is truly hard-nosed on crime."

The Judge headed back to Palos Verdes after the press conference. He drove to Sepulveda, a.k.a. the Pacific Coast Highway. But soon, he found himself in a colossal traffic jam as crowded as the damn L.A. freeway, inching his way snail-like south in his Mercedes convertible.

There seemed more and more people, more and more cars, and less and less space, every time he turned around. He wished they'd all go back home, to where they came from. Let L.A. regress to its former relaxed state that only the old Angelo natives could recall. But it wasn't to be. And the weather being so great, the Judge certainly wasn't going anywhere.

He was not going anywhere now, pedaling the break again. He finally cut down to the back streets of Hermosa Beach and plugged along there toward PV, pretending he was a local. As he left one of the many stop signs on his secret route, his cell phone went off, this time breaking into the sounds of 'Danny Boy', a cappella.

"This is the Judge," he croaked into the phone, wishing he had his water bottle.

"Hi Judge. It's Paul Ranger."

"Paul! It's been so long, I thought you'd died and gone to heaven."

"Nope, still practicing. Got a young wife and a son at USC, so I can't ever stop."

"You lucky duck, Paul. My son's not yet five; hasn't grown out of the terrible twos yet."

"So I heard, Judge. Good for you. But listen, I've only got a minute, and this is kind of a personal call."

"Okay, old friend, what's up?"

"Your buddies at the bar think you should drop your representation of the defendants in The Strand case and gracefully exit."

"But…"

"Wait a minute, Judge. Don't get mad. Just hear me out. The scuttlebutt is our lady D.A. has the case nailed to the floor, no cracks, no way to slip out. And the lead prosecutor, this Jay Armstrong, he's an O'Melveny attorney who left some years ago to play criminal lawyer, the best litigator in the D.A.'s department. He's tough and clever and detailed. And he knows how to create great rapport with jurors. Your clients are going down, Judge. The case is a loser, any way you slice it. It's not going to do your reputation any good to be on the losing side."

"But Paul, these people are entitled to have a lawyer defend them. As near as I can tell, they've done nothing wrong. Someone's got to stand up and defend their rights in court."

"The way we see it, Judge, your representation of Laura Wilson is tarnishing your brand as a lawyer. The press has started to paint you as a pervert, and now the local citizens group, 'Me Three', or 'Me Parents', or…"

"Me Too Parents."

"Yes. Well, whatever. Now they've taken up the cry about you as one of the adults potentially snapping dirty pictures of their kids, and worse. And we all remember you and Laura Wilson were torrid lovers a few years back. That may be an ethical conflict. I don't know. But it certainly won't look good when that news surfaces and the press and this Me Too Parents group start drawing conclusions."

"So, you think I'm going to be tarred and feathered in the press?"

"It's already started, Judge. Have you lost any clients because of it?"

"No"

"It's going to happen, Judge. There's going to be a rush for the door by every client in your book if you continue in this case."

"I appreciate your call, Paul. And I respect your concern about what the case might do to my law practice. I know this must be a difficult call to make, and I acknowledge your concerns are legitimate."

"Good."

"But I have to continue as defense counsel in this matter for Laura Wilson."

"But Judge. You're going to lose. And you know how you hate to lose."

"I may lose, Paul. But I have to do my best not to. It's how we're both built. And yes, we both hate to lose. But I must continue with this representation for a number of reasons. First, Laura Wilson's pretty much broke and can't hire anyone else. It's me or a young public defender.

Second, Laura and I are old friends. I can't just abandon an old friend, whatever the cost. Paul, if it were you in her shoes, and an unpopular case like this one spread out across the yellow press, I couldn't abandon you either. And I suspect you'd refuse to abandon me."

"You're right of course. I'd have to stick with you even on the bow of the Titanic as it nosed skyward."

"And finally, it's not fair to the justice system, which we've all sworn to do our best to uphold. She's entitled to the best representation she can obtain, and right now, in this time and place, it's me. I'm obligated as a lawyer, under all those fine principles we took so seriously, Paul, back when we were young men, to do my best for her. To not be swayed by fear of the hue and cry of mob, be they rabid press, angry parents, overly sensitive clients, or ambitious DAs desperately running for re-election."

"Okay, Judge. I've tried. You're as stubborn an S.O.B. as ever. This is pretty much what I told them you'd say. Good luck old boy, and keep your powder dry for this Jay Armstrong."

There was a click and the line went dead. The Judge smiled, but it was grim smile. Even his old buddies at law thought he was crazy.

CHAPTER 21

"Specialists from the Los Angeles County's Crime Lab are investigating a vacant lot where children from The Strand Pre-School said they saw animals killed and buried, in what prosecutors believe was a concerted effort to scare the children into silence. One parent at the site reported his five-year-old son said, "This is where they killed the animals, right here, and over there by that apple tree. That tree is where the Devil lives."

The Judge rolled out of bed with a groan, stumbled to the TV and shut it off. He didn't want to hear any more news about his case this morning. Katy popped up from her side of the bed, looked at the clock, then made a dive for the bathroom, beating the Judge by a mere foot and closing the door in his face. Damn, he'd have to use the toilet down the hall again. He did so, then decided he'd go back to bed for a little snooze, but it wasn't to be. Just as he was drifting off a sharp elbow in his ribs reminded him he had more important things to do. This was the day they were taking Ralphie to see the shrink.

The Minor's Refuge for Change Center was a sprawling one-story building in Old-Town Torrance, across the street from a car repair shop, and side by side with a war surplus store. Not fancy digs, but the rent must be cheap, mused the Judge. They pushed their way in through tired glass doors, clean but scratched and nicked, each holding one of Ralphie's hands. The

128

little guy had suddenly turned silent. He looked stressed. They walked into a small lobby with a tall counter in one corner manned by a young woman about twenty; she had the feel of an unpaid intern.

The Judge introduced himself and explained they had an appointment with Dr. George Gibson. They were directed to take a seat. Katy and the Judge settled into vinyl chairs, mock leather, divided by a blond coffee table strewn with magazines: Good Housekeeping, Allure, Family Circle, and a muscle car magazine thrown in for dads, all dog-eared and several months old. A large wooden box sat in the other corner filled with three wooden toy trucks and two well-loved dolls, one white and one black. Ralphie went for the trucks.

The Judge was only halfway through flipping the pages on muscle cars when the door behind the counter opened and a man stepped out, walked around the counter and extended a hand to Katy as the Judge rose.

Dr. Gibson was late thirties, tall, slender, and looking cool in all white, loose-fitting cotton slacks, and matching cotton top. He had a blond crewcut. He almost looked like a painted advertisement for a cool doctor shrink. But his soft smile was belied by the small frown lines etched around his jaw and the fine lines at the edges of his eyes that read stress and pain. His hazy brown eyes regarded the Judge with interest, subtly ignoring Katy. He intuitively knew who would be trouble; it wasn't Katy or Ralphie.

He bent down with a Cheshire-like smile to formally shake the hand of the little guy, who'd been called over by Katy, reluctantly abandoning his wooden truck which had been crashing pretty consistently into the side of the toy box, deepening a long-standing dent.

Ralphie looked up at Gibson suspiciously, unconsciously shifting his weight onto one foot and then the other. Gibson complimented Ralphie on his red and blue checked shirt and told him he looked like a fine young man. Ralphie puffed up a little at that, deciding Gibson was harmless.

The good doctor led them back through the door, down a long corridor with cubicles on either side, then small offices and interview rooms, and finally at the end to a large paneled door which opened silently on well-oiled hinges to expose Gibson's private office. Expensive wood paneling in distressed tongue and groove covered the walls and floor, over which a hand-knotted Indo Badami wool carpet was laid.

Degrees, certificates and awards alternating with pictures of far off places in India, Brazil and Australia spread across the walls, punctuated by a large window opposite the door looking out on a small fenced play yard, displaying a green artificial lawn with leafy plants defining its boarders and large plastic children's toys staged here and there in bright reds, yellows and blues.

After some polite chatter about the weather, the history of the center, and the importance of children's mental health, an assistant was buzzed in, an older woman with a kind face that lit up when she saw Ralphie. She took Ralphie back into the maze of offices and out a side door into the yard so he could examine the toys, placing him within the view of his parents, but out of earshot.

This was the signal for more serious conversation.

"I know you are anxious about Ralphie and what might have happened to him at The Strand Pre-School," Gibson said.

"We have no reason to think anything happened," said the Judge. Katy bit her lip.

"Of course. And perhaps nothing did. But it's important we check things out for Ralphie's sake."

"You don't believe it will traumatize Ralphie to interrogate him about what might have happened?" asked the Judge.

"No. We'll be very careful with your son."

"How will you go about questioning him?" asked the Judge.

"I'll first give Ralphie an opportunity to volunteer information about possible sexual abuse in a relaxed setting with these puppets." He pointed to a box of puppets sitting on an upper shelf of his book case. "But it's very likely Ralphie will not respond with information about sexual abuse. In my experience sexually abused children naturally try to avoid such touchy subjects. So, I'll then bring up the topic myself with Ralphie and see if we can find out what happened."

"If anything," corrected the Judge. "We want to be there and listen in."

"That's very unusual, and generally makes for a less productive session, Judge."

"I don't care. I want to see what's happening and be able to intercede if I'm concerned."

"Hmmm. Suppose you observe through a one-way mirror from an adjacent room. We have a room set up that way for teaching purposes."

"That will work."

"Great, let's get started."

As they stood up, Katy reached for the Judge's hand, taking it in a death grip.

Ralphie was brought back and they moved to a smaller room in the building: white walls, buff carpeting, no pictures, no toys, no distractions, except for the box of puppets Gibson brought in under one arm. Ralphie couldn't keep his eyes off the box.

A single large mirror was set in one wall. There were two cushioned table chairs with a small table beside them in the center of the room, and a tripod with a video camera set up behind one of them.

Ralphie was craning his head and standing on tiptoes, trying to get a better look at the puppets in Gibson's box. The Judge explained to Ralphie that Dr. Gibson would have a conversation with him, and that Mom and Dad would be in the next room, within shouting distance if he needed anything. Ralphie tensed up, worried, and noticeably gulped. But he nodded his head he understood.

An assistant appeared and escorted Katy and the Judge to a smaller room next door with more comfortable chairs, where the interview room could be viewed through the one-way glass, and where mics reported all conversation.

Gibson set the box down beside one chair and settled Ralphie in the other one, then turned on the video camera and sat down.

The first ten minutes were filled with chit-chat as Gibson established rapport, inquiring of Ralphie his favorite colors, what foods he liked, what toys he thought were best, what he wanted to do when he grew up, his best friend, and so on. Ralphie answered forthrightly, becoming more relaxed as he talked, but unable to keep his eyes off the box of puppets on the floor next to Gibson.

Finally, Gibson said, "I see you're wondering about my puppets, Ralphie. Would you like to see them?"

Ralphie nodded.

Gibson picked up a fat doll, which was all pink, wore no clothes, and sprouted red pubic hair. "We call this puppet Miss Laura, after Miss Laura at your school. And this doll," picking up a brawny looking male doll with a malevolent face, also all pink, no clothes, and with anatomically correct plumbing protruding from a ring of pubic hair, "we call Mr. Harry. And these two are fun, this one is Mr. Monkey, and this one is Mr. Alligator. Would you like to play a game with me and my puppets?"

Ralphie nodded.

"Here, let's give you Mr. Alligator to start, and I'll take Mr. Monkey."

He helped Ralphie put Mr. Alligator on his small hand.

"Mr. Monkey wants to hear about the games that were played at your school, you know, The Strand Pre-School. Do you remember the games you played?"

Mr. Alligator nodded yes.

133

Gibson said, "Some kids told me there were some naked games played there. Do you remember the naked games, Mr. Alligator?"

CHAPTER 22

Mr. Alligator sat still, not moving. The little hand holding the puppet inside tense and rigid, the tension extending out through Ralphie's tiny wrist.

"Oh, come now, Mr. Alligator, surely you remember the naked games?"

Mr. Alligator shook his head, "No."

Gibson leaned a little closer to Ralphie with his puppet, almost in an intimidating manner.

"My, my, Mr. Monkey thinks Mr. Alligator here is a little bit chicken. He says he can't remember any of the naked games. But we think you can, Mr. Alligator, 'cause we know naked games were played when you were around, 'cause the other kids told us. It's called the Naked Movie Star Game. Do you remember?"

Ralphie's puppet shook its head. "Um, I don't remember that game."

"Oh, now now, Mr. Alligator. Don't be shy. It may be a little yucky to talk about, but we know you were there Mr. Alligator."

"Umm, well, it's, umm, a little song that me and Mark heard."

"Oh?"

"Well, I heard someone singing, 'Naked Movie Star, Naked Movie Star.'"

"See, so you do know about that, Mr. Alligator. That means you're smart," Gibson's puppet said.

135

"Cause that's the same song the other kids knew and that's how we really know you're smarter than you look. So you better not play dumb with us, Mr. Alligator."

Mr. Alligator shook his head. But Ralphie looked worried now. He didn't want to be dumb.

"Well," Mr. Alligator said, "I didn't really hear it a whole lot. I just heard someone yell it from out in the…. Someone yelled it."

"Maybe, Mr. Alligator, you peeked in the window one day and saw them playing it, and maybe you could remember and help us."

'Well, no, I haven't seen anyone playing Naked Movie Star. I've only heard the song."

Gibson sat back in his chair while his Mr. Monkey gave an elaborate sigh. "What good are you, Mr. Alligator? You must be dumb."

"Well, I don't know really, umm, remember seeing anyone play that, 'cause I wasn't there, when… I… I mean when other kids were playing it."

"You weren't?... You weren't? I think you were. That's why we're thinking maybe you saw something. See, a lot of the puppets in this box weren't there, but they got to 'hear' what happened. But you. You were there. You saw."

"Well… I saw a lot of fighting."

"Oh come on now, Mr. Alligator, Mr. Monkey thinks you can help us a lot, 'cause, like, Naked Movie Star is a simple game. Because we know about that game. 'Cause we just had twenty kids tell us about that game. Just this morning, a little girl came in and played it for us and sang it just like that. Do you think if I asked you a question, you could put your thinking cap on and you might remember, Mr. Alligator?"

"Maybe."

"You could nod your head yes or no. Can you remember who took the pictures at the Naked Movie Star game? That would be a great thing to feed into this secret machine."

Gibson picked up a small toy video camera from out of his box with his other hand. "And then it would be all gone. That's what the other kids did. They felt a lot better after they fed what they saw into this secret machine. You can just nod whether you remember or not. Let's see how good your memory is, shall we Mr. Alligator?"

Ralphie's Mr. Alligator nodded its head.

"I wonder if you could hold this camera in your mouth, Mr. Alligator, and then you wouldn't have to say a word and Ralphie wouldn't have to say a word. And you could just point."

Gibson leaned over and helped Ralphie guide his puppet to place the toy camera in Mr. Alligator's mouth. Then Gibson held up the Mr. Harry doll, all pink and looking silly without clothes and no fig leaf.

"Did Mr. Harry use the camera at school, Mr. Alligator?"

"Sometimes he did."

"Can I pat you on the head for that?" Mr. Monkey reached over and patted Mr. Alligator on the head. "Look what a big help you can be, Mr. Alligator. You're going to help all these other children, because you're really smart. Okay, did the kids pose in funny poses for pictures for Mr. Harry's camera, Mr. Alligator?"

"Well, it wasn't a real camera. We just played…"

"Oh, and it went flash?"

"Well, it didn't go flash."

"It didn't go flash. Went click then? Did little pictures get taken?'

"I don't remember."

"Oh, you don't remember that. Well, you're still doing pretty good, Mr. Alligator. I've got to shake your hand."

Mr. Monkey reached over, removed the toy camera, and then shook Mr. Alligator's paw.

"Maybe you could show me with this, with this doll, how the kids danced for the Naked Movie Star game." Gibson held up the naked Mr. Harry doll and using Mr. Monkey, picked up another doll which was dressed.

"Well, they didn't really dance. It was just, like, a song."

"Well, what did they do when they sang the song?"

"They just went around and sang the song."

"They just went around and sang the song?"

Mr. Alligator nodded his head.

"And they took their clothes off?"

Mr. Alligator shook his head no.

"I heard the kids did. I heard from several different kids in your class that they took their clothes off. That's kind of a hard secret, it's kind of a yucky secret to talk about. But, maybe, maybe we could see if we could find…"

"I don't remember that," interrupted Mr. Alligator.

"Okay. Okay then. Tell you what. Let's play with different puppets. This is my favorite puppet right here."

Gibson put down Mr. Monkey and picked up a bird puppet. "You want to try Mr. Bird?"

Ralphie's face brightened; he nodded an assent.

Gibson removed Mr. Alligator and replaced it with Mr. Bird over the small hand.

"Okay, Ralphie? Then I get to be Detective Dog...."

Gibson pulled a dog puppet out of his box and put it on. Then he pulled two new dolls out of his box with his other hand, one a little boy and one a little girl. The puppets were pink and nude, anatomically correct, with no pubic hair. He set them on the small table between them.

"I know we're goanna figure this out... all this stuff. We're going to figure it out right now. We're going to just figure it all out. Okay? When that tricky part about touching the kids was going on, could you take a pointer in your beak Mr. Bird and point on the... on the dolls here, on either one of these dolls, where... where the kids were touched? Could you do that?" Gibson picked a short piece of doweling from his box and leaned forward to place it in Mr. Bird's beak.

"I don't know," said Mr. Bird.

"I know the kids were touched. Let's see if we can figure this out."

"I don't know," Mr. Bird said again.

"You don't know where they were touched?"

"Uh-uh," Mr. Bird shook its head.

"Well, some of the kids told me that they were touched sometimes. They said it was, it was kinda, sometimes it kinda hurt. And some of the times, it felt pretty good. Do you remember that touching game?"

"No."

"Okay. Let me see if we can try something else and--."

"No." Ralphie spun the bird puppet above his head, making it fly. "Wheeee!"

"Come on, bird, get down here and help us out," said Detective Dog.

"No."

"Well Mr. Bird, it looks like Ralphie's having a hard time talking. But I don't wanna hear any more 'No's. No more 'No's. Detective Dog is gonna figure this out. Did anybody put something yucky in your mouth? Like say, Mr. Harry."

Ralphie just looked at Gibson, uncertain.

"Can you remember?" prompted Detective Dog.

"I'm not sure."

"How about a finger in your hole?"

Ralphie's puppet nodded.

"Boy, well there you go. See how smart you are."

Ralphie just looked at Gibson.

"What else did Mr. Harry do?"

Ralphie sat a little straighter, putting Mr. Bird in his lap.

"He never did that stuff," he said.

That's when the door flew open and the Judge bounded into the room.

"I think we've heard enough, Dr. Gibson. Come on Ralphie, we're leaving."

The argument with Katy started later that evening, after Ralphie had been tucked into bed. It started small, Katy merely saying that perhaps the Judge reacted too quickly to terminate Dr. Gibson's interview with Ralphie.

"Katy, that was a crock of shit. Gibson was asking leading questions, telegraphing what testimony he wanted fed back from our son, whether it actually happened or not."

"Listen, Judge. It wasn't a court of law in there. Your rules of evidence don't apply. We're dealing with emotions, nuisances, impressions from our son, memories he may not want to share. Trying to coax out what really happened."

"Yeah, whether anything happened or not."

"Dr. Gibson is well respected in his field. He has lots of experience with molested children. I'm the high school counselor here, not you. This is my field of study. And Gibson's methods are documented. Children are reluctant, even embarrassed, to admit they've been molested. They suffer feelings of guilt and shame. Gibson's methods give them the opportunity to unburden themselves."

"His methods are a script, prepared to elicit what he wants to hear."

"Just like you Judge. You're listening to your own script on this now, hearing only what you want to hear. Suppose our son has been molested. Now we'll never learn the truth."

"I don't believe Ralphie's been molested."

"But you don't know, do you Judge? You don't know." Katy's voice was rising now, an octave at a time. "If Ralphie was molested, he may be facing a lifetime of shame and anguish, a lifetime of trying to work through thoughts and stresses buried in the prism of his childhood memories that he can never quite understand because it's all repressed. You may have denied our Ralphie his one chance to find a way out, Judge."

"I can't believe that guy's technique, trying to badger Ralphie into saying things Gibson thinks happened, has any merit," said the Judge, rising now from his protective seat to face Katy, his voice rising.

"But Gibson's seen the other kids, Judge. He knows what went on better than anyone, certainly better than you!"

"Does he, Katy? Or does he just have his own personal demons he needs to promulgate, and then placate in the unfinished minds of the small children entrusted to his care?"

Suddenly there was a noise behind them. They turned to see Ralphie peeking out at them from the hall, standing in his pajamas with feet, rubbing his eyes, looking like one of Pan's Lost Boys. Annie the Dog stood behind him, her muzzle pressed against his side. He looked up at his two towering parents, flushed with argument, and whispered, "Please don't yell anymore."

Then he turned and receded back down the hall toward his room, dragging his favorite blankie behind him. Annie the Dog gave them both a single reproachful look, then turned and trailed Ralphie back toward his bedroom.

CHAPTER 23

The Judge was high in a cave, looking down from his over-rock perch. A small fire below up-lighted with an unholy glow the chiseled faces of Ralphie and Laura Wilson, both nude, Ralphie's tiny under-nourished chest contrasting with Laura's ponderous swinging breasts. They danced around the fire in a four-some: Ralphie, Mr. Alligator, Laura and Mr. Monkey, singing over and over, "*What you see is what you are... We're all naked Movie Stars!*"

The Judge awoke from the nightmare with a start, covered with sweat, as his TV alarm went off with a crack.

"*One young man, age five, says he was taken to a farm where he watched Harry Wilson beat and kill a horse with his bare hands, and then to a Circus House where people were dressed in elephant costumes.*

A young girl reports she was taken to a church several times for candle-lit ceremonies where black-robed hooded adults stood in a circle around her and moaned. The last time there, Harry Wilson cut a live rabbit open, warning, "If you tell anyone of the secrets that happened in The Strand or here, then this will happen to you!"

All this press coverage was giving him nightmares he mused, telling himself that was all it was; nothing to do with any uncertainty that Ralphie had not been molested. He got out of bed and slammed the TV off, heading for his shave and shower. He had a busy day planned at his Venice office.

As he pulled down his driveway to leave there was a Palos Verdes police car sitting at the bottom, parked, waiting. Perhaps for him. It was unclear. As he pulled past the officer ignored him. But as he watched in his review mirror, the cop got on his radio and made a call, then started up and followed him down the hill, across the front of Malaga Cove Plaza and to the city limits. He'd just been escorted out of his own city. Damn!

Worse, as he crossed into the small jigsaw of South Torrance there was a Torrance Police cruiser there waiting. It escorted him out to Pacific Coast Highway, where he turned north, and followed him to the boundary with Redondo Beach. There a Redondo Beach cruiser picked up his tail.

He dropped left off PCH after the Redondo Beach Harbor sign, picking up his secret route that snaked through Hermosa Beach along Ardmore Avenue, picking up a Hermosa Beach cruiser along the way which escorted him to the Ocean Hill City boundary. There, crossing 1st street and continuing along Ardmore, jogging a block south to pick up Valley Drive at 15th Street, he was tailed by an Ocean Hill Police car. This quiet route, worthy of Waze, would take him all the way to Dockweiler Beach and into Playa Vista, steps from Venice, without traffic. But he had the feeling he wouldn't make it that far. He was right.

A block past the Ocean Hill Police station at 15th, the cruiser behind him turned on its flashing lights, pulling him over into the side parking on Valley Drive.

A moment later a second car pulled up, an ordinary sedan except for the mounted flashing light in its back window, and Detective Oliver Hardy moved his ponderous bulk out of it, swaying slightly as he walked on the balls of his feet up to the Judge's car, displaying a belligerent gait worthy of East L.A.

The Judge rolled his window down and Hardy leaned into it, forcing the Judge to lean away, toward the passenger side of his car, trying to avoid the scent of bacon and onions that had accompanied Hardy's breakfast.

"So, Judge. Visiting our fair city again, are we?"

"I'm on route to my office in Venice. What's the   problem?"

"It's you, Judge. You're the problem. See we don't like sexual perps in our city. I haven't decided whether you're a sexual perp… or just a fellow traveler, an accommodator so to speak, but either way you're not welcome here."

"You're talking about the Wilsons and The Strand Pre-School?"

"Hooray, Judge. You're smarter than you look. That's exactly what I'm talking about."

"Look, Detective. I'm only doing my job. I'm a lawyer. I defend people caught in the Justice System."

"Some people don't deserve to be defended, Judge. Some people are so guilty you can smell it on them. You can smell their fear. They just need to be caged like the animals they are."

"Without a trial? Without due process? Without a chance to confront their accusers? Without an opportunity to dispute the allegations, provide contrary evidence, explain their actions?"

145

"These Wilsons are guilty as hell and you know it. They should fry. And you're helping them try to wiggle out of the consequences of what they've done. They've brought enormous grief and pain to many innocent young lives, like... like... like my daughter's. That makes you equally culpable in a lot of people's eyes."

"In yours."

"Yes, in mine. I want you to walk away from this case, Judge. Leave it. Let someone else handle it who doesn't like to drive through my city so often, enjoy our hospitality, expect to be treated civilly here while they gut everything we stand for. And a lot of people here feel the same way as I do about you."

"So, this is a warning? Or a threat?"

"Call it what you want, Judge. You continue on with these Wilsons and I'll see to it you'll never get another law client from here in Ocean Hill again, or from Hermosa, or Redondo, or Palos Verdes. We know who you are Judge, and we know what you're about. The South Bay is a tight-knit community. You continue to represent these perps and one way or another you're going to get buried. We'll spread your reputation for defending trash far and wide. No one's going to want to do business with you. You better plan on finding another place to live, maybe in another state, where people don't know the kind of person you are and the ugly things you do."

Hardy stood up from his window lean, gave the Judge a final flashing look through angry eyes, spun on his heel, and stomped his bulk back to his car.

The Judge sat immobile in his car for a minute, hands clutching the steering wheel, finding it difficult to deal with his anger. He knew police work often attracted certain personalities, particularly bullies who enjoyed the power over people that came with the uniform and the holstered gun. Those sorts liked to throw their power around, often making life miserable for law-abiding citizens just trying to get by. And they often got away with their terrorizing tactics in the poorer communities of Los Angeles. But those tactics mostly didn't work with lawyers trained to stand up to police, stand up to prosecutors, stand up to judges. Tasked with protecting their clients and assuring individual rights were protected under the country's imperfect justice system.

Detective Hardy would not get away with his not so subtle threat against a defense counsel. The Judge wasn't sure how he'd do it, but Hardy would have to pay for his crude attempt to undermine the justice system. Such conduct could not be tolerated. It had to be stamped out. Everyone had to play by the agreed rules or the system was worthless.

CHAPTER 24

The Judge awoke to another blast from his TV as its alarm turned on the morning newscast. Katy was already gone.

"Folks, this is a special investigatory news show this morning. We're going to be delving deep into The Strand Pre-School molestations. We're going to show you how to protect your children against sexual abuse in school," Intoned the famous news commentator who was show anchor.

He held up what he claimed was a police report identifying Harry Wilson as an accused pedophile. Video ran of prosecutor Armstrong talking about the children's frightening stories, and how they'd been drugged. This was followed by a second video showing how Dr. George Gibson had cleverly used hand puppets to draw the molestation stories from the children. The show then cut to bizarre drawings that some children had made, depicting The Strand Pre-School staff and laced with sexual connotations, at least in the eyes of the commentator.

At this point the Judge had had enough, slamming the TV off and heading for the shower. Today the Judge was going to track down a surfer friend of Jeffrey's. What was the guy's name? Matt? Yes, it was Matt, Matt... Singer. The Judge checked his scribbled notes to be sure. A few calls later he had a line on where Matt Singer liked to surf during the week.

Late that afternoon the Judge sat in his car and watched the sun settle below the pier, slowly dipping the bottom of its orange orb into distant water. The sea was dark blue now except where the sun's rays cut a yellow streak across the water, right up to the foam of the waves sliding onto the beach. The sky above was darkening too, cloudless, shifting to a darker half-light blue.

As he got out of his car in the lot a voice rang out to his left.

"Hi, Judge."

Shit, it was Bradford Jones, the Daily Mirror reporter.

"I have it from a credible source that the Wilsons took The Strand kids to the local market right here in Ocean Hill. They invited some like-minded friends in and molested the hell out of the tots in the backroom between the stacks of soda. Any comment?"

"How do you define a 'credible source', Jones?"

"Like the dictionary, Ace. 'Credible source' means from someone I can trust and believe."

"You spoke to a kid who says he was taken into the backroom of the market and molested?"

"No, but…"

"Someone who was there in the backroom of the market and watched?"

"Well… no."

"Someone who saw the kids taken into the backroom of the market?"

"No."

"Go away, Jones. Your 'credible sources' give me a headache."

The Judge turned away and trudged down to the beach. A clutch of surfers, mid-thirties, their wetsuits stripped down to their hips, chatted idly, pulling their gear together, preparing to abandon the beach now the waves had softened to puddle size. The Judge walked over and asked, "Anybody here know Matt Singer?"

"That's me," said a redhead at the back, tall, brown eyes, sporting a short sandy beard and a robust chest of sandy hair. He was lifting his board to depart.

"Can I talk to you for just a few minutes?" the Judge asked.

"What about?"

"Jeffrey Simpson."

The smile left Singer's face immediately, replaced
by caution.

"You police?"

"No. I'm part of the defense team defending
the
 Wilsons in this Strand Pre-School thing. I was a judge once, so folks mostly just call me Judge."

The Judge brought the corners of his mouth up
into his best boy scout smile and opened his eyes wide and innocent, extending his hand to shake, not flinching at the sandy paw he got.

"Jeffrey didn't have anything to do with that."

"I know. But he worked there, and now he's dead. I'm just trying to figure out what happened. Whether it was suicide... or something else."

"I guess we can talk. Let's sit over there." Matt pointed to a bench near the pier entrance. They strolled together across the sand. Singer leaned his board against a concrete anchor buried in the sand where he could keep an eye on it.

"How was the surfing today?" the Judge asked.

"Any kind of surfing is good, as long as it's me doing it. It was a light day. You surf?"

"No. Always wanted to, but never seemed to be the time. And of course, I'm not very coordinated. I have difficulty walking."

Singer smiled. Nodded his head. "It's not for everyone. But it's addictive. It's now officially California's State Sport."

"You down here a lot on your board?"

"Yeah. I'm the morning shift manager for the supermarket here in town. Leaves me time to be down here in the afternoons. What'd you want to know about Jeff?"

"You think he killed himself, Matt?"

"Sure. I mean, I don't know. How would I know? But that's what the paper said."

"But you knew him?"

Singer gave a big sigh. "Yeah, I knew him I guess. To the extent you really know anyone. I knew him casually. We shared some great waves up and down the coast."

"Someone told me you were best buddies."

"Who told you that? I wouldn't say that. We were just casual friends."

"Did Jeff have any other surfer friends?"

"I don't know. I think there was another guy. Asian. Not sure who he was but I saw them together some."

"Know of any other friends of Jeff's?"

"No. I don't. He was kind of a difficult guy."

"How so?"

"Short tempered. Got angry easily. Foul mouth when he was angry. He was always running off. Cursing the waves, cursing his board, cursing me for being in his path. Acted like the whole damn universe was out to get him."

"But you spent time with him anyway?"

"Some. Felt a little sorry for him. Being a vet and all. Seemed like he didn't get treated very well by the system."

"So, you did know him pretty well?"

"No. I wouldn't say that. About five weeks ago I caught him going through my wallet, taking some of my cash. I called him on it. We didn't speak much after that."

"What happened?"

"I was in my wetsuit. Asked him to watch my stuff while I went to take a leak. For some reason when I got to the door of the toilet I looked back. Instinct or something. There he was yanking my wallet out of my jacket."

"What'd you do?"

"I just stood there. I was in shock. Watched him take two large bills out of my wallet, then shove it back into my pants."

"What then?"

Took my leak, came back out. He was preparing to leave. I called him to wait, marched over, told him to give my money back or I'd call the police."

"Did he give it back?"

"Not at first. Got angry. Said I was a liar. Rattled off a few of his favorite epithets at me. The other surfers packing up turned to watch. I got my cell phone out, was going to call Nine-One-One."

"And?"

"He reached into his back pocket and threw my two bills down on the sand at my feet, said it wasn't worth the fuss. Then he shot me the finger and stomped off."

"You see him again after that?"

"No. I mean, I saw him around. But we didn't speak."

"Why'd he need the money?"

"He always needed money. Was always mooching drinks or a burger or whatever he could mooch. He found it tough to support his drug habit I think. He was very moody. Almost bi-polar. He was an okay surfer, but not someone I wanted to hang with on the beach after he took my money."

"Who did he mostly hang with after that?"

"No one much, except that Asian guy. And of course, he always had that damn dog."

"Tell me about the dog."

"More of a mutt really. Mix of cocker and something, grey eyes, old, moved slow. But Jeff loved that dog. Loved it more than people I'd say."

"Know any reason why someone would want to kill the dog?"

"The dog? No. But it did die. I heard somebody
hit it on a motorcycle. Jeff took it hard."

"Did Jeff have any other friends, maybe non-surfing buddies, you know about?"

"A brother, I think his name's Erwin. Lives on The Strand. And his ex-wife. Jeff used to bitch about her all the time, even when he was sober."

"Anyone else?"

"Oh, there was an old army buddy he liked to hang with. Sam something, Sam Reynolds. Met him once. Didn't seem very friendly. Kind of a sour guy. Maybe that's why he and Jeff got along."

"Anybody else you recall?

"Back, just before our altercation, I saw Jeff walking along The Strand in a serious conversation with some guy, older, grey hair, wore a white lab coat. Couldn't hear what it was about, but the guy seemed to know Jeff well, put his hand on Jeff's shoulder a couple of times, like he was giving him advice. Fatherly.

"Anyone else?"

"Yeah. More recently I saw Jeff arguing with a guy up in North Ocean Hill. Looked like a dangerous guy, not the sort I'd want to cross. But hell, Jeff argued with everyone, and he was always yelling about something."

"Where'd you see them?"

"I saw them on The Strand. Below 40th Street. I nodded at Jeff as I went past on my bike, but he ignored me."

"What did the guy look like?"

"Maybe thirty, tall, white, had a flak jacket with bulging pockets and a hard face. Looked like he'd been around the block a few times."

"Did Jeff ever have an interest in child pornography? Have pictures, watch movies, follow young kids around?"

"No. Not that I ever saw."

The Judge thanked Singer for his time, shoved his hands into his pockets to protect from what was turning into a biting cold evening, and trudged back to his car.

CHAPTER 25

"At the urging of affected parents and the 'Me Too Parents' movement, L.A. Crime Lab specialists have begun digging up the ground around The Strand Pre-School, and in the adjacent vacant lot, looking for tunnels and other evidence of the Satanic rituals and the molestations that occurred there. The children have said there's an apple tree in the vacant lot that was the focus of Satanic rituals to which they were subjected. They say that's where the Devil lives."

The Judge shook himself out of the lingering shreds of his sleep and stumbled from his bed to the TV to turn it off. The newscasters were relentless in their braying about The Strand Pre-School and the alleged molestation that went on there. The newspapers and radio were no better, pounding on the Wilsons day after day, wave after wave of coverage that assumed their guilt. One of the documentary news shows was doing another program on The Strand and the allegations of kiddy abuse, with guest appearances by angry parents and one of the allegedly damaged kids. The kid would certainly be damaged after he got off that show, thought the Judge.

The Judge checked his list of people associated with Jeffrey Simpson. Sam Reynolds, the army buddy was next up. The Judge called a friend at the Department of Defense who was able to run down the name and match it to a guy who had been in Simpson's unit overseas and now lived in Hermosa Beach. It had to be the same guy. There was an address, but there was no phone number. The Judge figured he'd work till three in his Venice office and then swing by.

Sam Reynolds wasn't home at four p.m., but his neighbor in the small triplex where he lived said at this time of day the Judge would probably find Reynolds down on the beach playing sand volleyball with his team. They played at the end of 10th Street.

By the time the Judge found a parking spot and got down to the beach, the men's volleyball team had finished. The women's volleyball team was in spirited progress. Amazing young bodies, slender muscular legs, tight butts, long arms and small breasts, decked out in close-fitting one piece red or blue swimsuits, throwing themselves up in the air, twisting this way and that, pounding the ball back down across the net with fury. Magnificent animals all.

Watching made his blood run. He was way too old to catch a glance in this group, but he was still male. Thoughts of Katy disappeared completely from the lizard part of his brain as he enjoyed their display, which seemed mostly directed at a clutch of young men, bare chested, leaning against surfboards or sitting in sand chairs at the edge of the court. Similarly absorbed.

He scanned the crowd, spotting the men's team, all guys a little older, wearing matching blue trunks and t-shirts, huddled behind one end of the sand court. The Judge maneuvered his way through the small crowd to the group and asked for Sam Reynolds. He was pointed to a tall man, early thirties, over six foot, muscular, sitting on the sand, arms grasping his knees, rocking slightly with the ebb and flow of the women's game, obviously enjoying himself. The Judge settled down in the sand next to Reynolds, mirroring his position, and whispered, "Who's ahead?"

"Ocean Hill right now, but we're going to take them."

"You're for Hermosa?"

"Damn straight." He smiled, giving the Judge a closer look.

"You're Sam Reynolds."

"I am. Who's asking?" He had Reynolds' full attention now, his eyes narrowing, the young bodies careening in mid-flight against the net suddenly forgotten.

"They call me 'Judge'. I'd like to talk to you for a few minutes after the game if I might."

"About what?"

"Jeffrey Simpson."

"You police?"

"No. Attorney for Laura Wilson."

"Jeffie and I were friends. But I don't know noth'n about who killed him."

"I'm just trying to understand a little more about Jeffrey. Who he was. What he was like. See if I can figure what happened, and why. Just take a minute."

"You buying the beer?"

"I am."

"Okay. Let's watch the match now."

Reynolds was right. After being down by four points, the Hermosa women put on an amazing display of death-defying dives and smashing net shots to come back and win, barely. After a hefty applause from the young men camped at the edges of the court, the Judge and Reynolds got up and wandered over to Barnacles Bar & Grill, settling in at a table. Reynolds ordered an expensive craft beer; the Judge stuck with his favorite, Dos Equis.

"So, you and Jeffrey were friends?"

"More than friends, we were mates in Afghanistan. I was in the truck with him when we got hit."

"Can you tell me about it?"

"What, the war? Afghanistan? I don't like to think about it."

"It may be important to understanding what happened to Jeffrey."

Reynolds sighed. "You ever serve, Judge?"

"The military? No. I missed that opportunity."

"You're a lucky son of a bitch, Judge. It ain't no opportunity. It's a ticket to Hell; for some a one-way ticket."

"What did you serve as?"

"I was going to be a Ranger, clandestine water work and shit. But I washed out after six months. I ended up being a butt-class medic. Turned experience into a nursing degree and got a good gig now working in a hospice."

"Can you tell me what happened when you and Jeffrey got hit over there?"

Reynolds's eyes drifted away from the Judge, out over the Judge's shoulder, to the street, and beyond. His face lost all expression, except for his mouth, which tightened into a thin line. After a minute of silence, the Judge waiting him out, he turned his eyes back on the Judge, pain in them now.

"It was a fuckin' clusterfuck if ever there was. Six years now, and my memories are still fractured. Blood spraying everywhere, Jimmy's guts squirming across my knees, warm and wet. Jimmy just looking at his intestines, staring, unbelieving. Tony in the back screaming for his mother. Jeffie puking his K rations all over the steering wheel and me. The smell of crap, blood, vomit, burning tires, and…. Fear. I can still taste the fear.

I have nightmares still, wake up in a cold sweat, screaming. I wish I could let it go, get it out of my head, but it's always there, in the back of my consciousness, wherever I turn. Like some giant black bag that drops over me, engulfing me for an instant in darkness, then spewing it all out again inside my head, all the sounds, the lights, the smells…the terror."

Reynolds collected himself for a moment. He took a deep breath. "We were in a convoy of three trucks, cutting through a side street, a short-cut to get out of this fuckin' village we had to go through to reach our base with supplies. We were in the lead truck, Jeffie was driving, I had the middle seat, and Jimmy, my best bud, was against the window, hanging partly out.

It was so damn hot. Tony and Penn were up in the truck bed behind, Penn manning a machine gun on a swivel. It was a narrow dusty street between buildings three stories high, some of them partially destroyed. There'd been a fire-fight there two days before.

Sarge was out in front of our truck, walking briskly, watching the road. None of it felt right."

"And it all came apart?"

Reynolds nodded. "Sarge shouted over the intercom, 'Stop, stop for a minute.' Jeffie and I'd been up late, playing poker. We were both tired. Anyway, Jeffie just keeps driving, like Sarge hadn't said anything. Like he hadn't heard, or he was in a daze or something.

Sarge screams, 'Stop the mother-fucking truck!'

Jeffie wakes up, slams his foot down, but hits the accelerator instead. The truck lurches forward. Sarge jumps sideways, to the left, almost gets his foot run over."

Reynolds' face was grim now, his eyes on a distant street in another world thousands of miles away. He folded his arms around himself, leaning forward a little, tightening their grip, as though to hold on.

"What happened?" the Judge prompted.

"It was an IED, right front tire rolled right over it. An enormous explosion, brilliant light, heat singed the back of my eyes, inside my lungs, compression of air and flying metal all around us, flames, acid fumes, we couldn't breathe.

Blew the fuck out of the cab and Jimmy, blasted his guts everywhere. Shrapnel went through the side of the truck, killing Penn instantly, putting metal the size of a monkey wrench into Tony's stomach. I got cut glass in one eye. looking through a stream of blood, gashed my head, sticky red running down my neck under my shirt."

"And Jeff?"

"Didn't get touched. Like he was Superman or something. Just sat there staring in horror, stunned, frozen in time, couldn't move."

"Sarge picked himself up on the driver's side of the truck. He was ballistic, screaming at Jeff. 'You dumb mother fuck son of a bitch. You killed us you shit-hole. You asshole son of a bitch.' Jumped up on the running board and tried to crawl in through the window to reach Jeffie, wanted to throttle him.

Sergeant from the truck behind pulled Sarge off the truck. Jeff is leaning over against me, away from the window and Sarge, puking all over me and the seat. I was in shock I think. Everything moved in slow motion. Watching... listening to Jimmy die as they tried to ease him out of the seat beside me; slipping on blood, intestines and his shit spilling out as they moved him. Tony screaming with the hole in his stomach. Penn just quiet, not with us anymore. Lucky, I guess."

"What'd Jeff do?"

"His face was grey. Looked like he was having a stroke or something. He got out, slid down against rubble in the street, took his helmet off, didn't say a word, just stared at his boots. Sarge came back, kicked at his boots, told him and me to get us assess in the back of the truck behind."

"They got you out of there?"

"Eventually. They loaded us on the second truck in back. Laid Jimmy and Penn beside us, put khaki sheets over them. Then they brought Tony, still alive, crying and retching as the truck started up. Moaning he didn't want to die. We watched, smelt, practically tasted the pooling liquid under the bodies, piss, poop, blood, stomach bile. Tried to hang on as we bounced over broken roads for forty-five minutes. Finally got to the base. Tony gave one last mighty sigh half way there and then went quiet. He didn't make it.

Jeffie was never the same after. Guess I wasn't either. They shipped me home right away, Jeffie a week later. Said we had battle fatigue."

"How'd you and Jeff hook up again?'

"I'm from El Segundo, Jeffie's from… was from Lomita. We both liked to surf. We just ran into each other at the VA, and then again one day on the beach. Agreed to stay close, 'cause of what we'd been through. That was about two months ago. We've gotten drunk together, smoked weed together, laid a few girls together. It's helped."

"So, you were both going to the VA. Getting help for PTSD?"

"Yeah. Jeffie said it was a waste of time, but he'd still go with me. I sure miss the bastard."

"Did Jeffrey have a drug issue?"

"Don't we all… We're vets. You sent us over there to kill people, risk getting killed, live in a heighten stress condition twenty-four seven, watch our buddies get shot up, die, wondering if it's our time next, uncertain of what we're supposed to be dying for.

Then finally we're pulled out, dumped out of the army and into the states, no job, no civilian training, no prospects. We come back here as battle tested veterans, but nobody gives a shit. Not really a war, we're told. Not very important to anybody what's going on in Afghanistan. Not important we risked our lives, lost our youth. People here don't have any better idea why we're in that Godforsaken country than we did when we were over there trying to stay alive. It's all just shit."

"Did Jeff feel like that too?"

"We all do. That's probably why he killed himself. Probably couldn't take it anymore."

"Know anyone who might want to see him dead?'

"Oh, now you're talking. You'd have to take a ticket."

"Really?"

"'Fraid so."

"Like who?"

"His ex-wife, for the insurance. She hates his guts. The ex- wife's boyfriend, a Class A hanger-on, jealous as hell of Jeffie. His older brother, Edwin or something, always jealous of Jeffie. That's just to name a few. And then there was the drug dealer."

"The drug dealer?"

"Yeah, Jeffie owed money to a drug dealer, or so he told me. He didn't have the money to pay the guy."

"How about you?"

"Me?

"Did you want to see him dead?"

"I've got a bad eye 'cause of that incident. You can't tell, can you. They did a pretty good job. My team only lets me play the left side of the volleyball court." Reynolds giggled, then he said, "I don't hold no grudge against anyone. Wasn't anyone's fault, what happened. It's a war for Christ sakes. We try to kill them. They try to kill us."

The Judge shook Reynolds' hand. "Thanks for talking with me, Sam."

"Let me know what you find out, Judge."

"I will."

The Judge picked up the tab and ordered Reynolds a second beer before sliding out, leaving him there staring into his drink, reliving the old memories their conversation had stirred.

CHAPTER 26

As the Judge walked into his house that evening, Katy was waiting for him inside the hall. "We've got to talk, Judge. Now!" She directed him into the living room by vigorously crooking her index finger. Jesus! Why did she always have to jump him as soon as he came through the front door, tired and stressed from a day's work?

He gave a lofty sigh, set his brief case down in the hall, and slouched across the living room to the comparative safety of his favorite chair, an old beat up leather with real arms. It'd seen better days. But he refused to let her give it to the Goodwill. It was his one small piece of resistance in a residence that she'd entirely remade during their marriage. Christ, nesting females were a menace.

"Judge, you've got to quit this Laura Wilson case, and you've got to do it now."

"I can't do that, Katy. Laura Wilson is entitled to the best defense against these charges that can be made."

"But why do you have to make it?"

"It's what I do, Katy. It's who I am. It's the oath I took as a lawyer. And Laura Wilson's a long-time family friend. If I don't step forward, who will?

Some light-weight public defender who has fifty other cases, overworked and underpaid?"

"What about me, Judge? What about the oath you took to me when we married, to honor and protect? You have no idea how it is here at home. Old friends spot me in the aisle of the supermarket and turn, fleeing in the other direction.

Faculty at school suddenly don't have time for lunch. Parents come into the school office and look through my door at me with stink-eyes. The teller at the bank avoids eye contact now. Ralphie is getting picked on in his new pre-school because of your Wilson case. Our neighbors on either side here in PV aren't speaking to me because of it. My book group quietly suggested perhaps I should attend to other matters and skip their meetings until this Strand Pre-School thing blows over."

"Katy, I just can't do it."

"Listen, Judge, the principal at the high school insisted on lunch yesterday, off campus. He whispered the School Superintendent wanted to convey, off the record of course, his concern about my husband's involvement in The Strand case.

I asked him, 'What the hell does that mean exactly?' He couldn't give me a straight answer. And earlier in the week I got an anonymous hate note at school in my counseling office, likely from some student. This is impacting my career as a high school counselor."

"This is America, Katy. The Wilsons are entitled to the presumption of innocence, until proven guilty. I can't give up Laura's case just because my clients are unpopular."

"This is more than unpopular, Judge. These people are monsters who abused little kids. Maybe even our Ralphie."

"Ralphie wasn't abused."

"We can't be sure of that. But that's not the point. You're destroying the reputation of your own family in the community by stubbornly insisting on defending this, this... woman. And it doesn't just end with the end of this case and these people getting their just deserts. Long after the case is done, people are going to have lingering grudges against you, against me, against Ralphie, for what you've done. We're becoming pariahs in the community."

"You're assuming Laura's guilty, just like everyone else, and she hasn't even been tried."

"Judge... what planet are you on? I know you read the newspapers, watch the TV. She's as guilty as hell. It's all over the news what she and her brother did." Katy's voice was up several octaves now, as was her volume.

"Pure yellow journalism, Katy. So much of what they're reporting is just pure speculation and misinformation. This rumor or that rumor is seized upon and held up as fact when there's been absolutely no evidence discovered to support it. The news people are building their networks on the backs of the Wilsons, sensationalizing tidbits of information, much of it false, gouged out of people who should know better than to talk at this early stage of the proceedings."

"That's bullshit, and you know it, Judge. You and your damn ego. You're just goddamn enjoying the attention of it all, leaving Ralphie and I with shattered relationships in the community, left to pick up the pieces after this is all over. You suck."

Katy was sputtering now. But she stopped herself, held her hand up, palm in his face to stop him from responding, controlling her breathing, slowing her heart rate as she'd been taught to do in one of her counseling classes, her eyes bulging a little with the effort.

Finally, in a lower, calmer voice, she got out, "Look Judge, even the District Attorney is certain they're guilty. And the sitting judge in the case. He's refused bail."

"For Christ sakes, Katy. That's the D.A.'s job. These days D.A.s over-charge everything and everyone. They can't ever afford to look soft on crime. If you accidentally drop a candy wrapper out the window and get caught, they'll charge you for obstruction of traffic, creating a public hazard on the road, road-rage, pollution of the environment, and even destruction of a species if they can tie the wrapper into some local problem with a butterfly or a frog.

Besides, Nancy Aragon is at the start of a strongly contested re-election campaign for her office, facing a challenger better organized, better funded and better liked. She's going to do anything to grab headlines, keep the public's attention, give the appearance she's tough on crime. To my mind she's just another bloated toad."

"And the sitting judge?"

"Ferguson? He's in the same boat. Coming up for re-election as a superior court judge, probably afraid he'll get dumped if he makes an unpopular call in The Strand case."

"More bullshit, Judge. These people are quite competent. They're both convinced the Wilsons are guilty. And they should know. They have access to all the facts."

"I have access to all the facts to date, Katy. And the known facts don't tie Laura and Harry Wilson to molestation of children at The Strand Pre-School."

"What about the testimony of all these kids, Judge? You think that's just made-up facts too?"

"You saw what Gibson tried to do to Ralphie. Lead him along into a story Gibson wanted to hear. No... the testimony of these children is not credible. And that's even before we get to trial, and Barney and I have an opportunity to cross examine what these kids now say after being brainwashed by Gibson."

"Look, Judge, you've got to stop. Even my mother's on the phone every morning, demanding I make you dump this case and stop ruining our lives."

"Oh, great. Now it's your mother, Florence, who decides which cases I'm allowed to take in my law practice." The Judge's voice was rising too.

"She'd choose better than you do, Judge," Katy shot back.

Katy stamped her foot on the floor, never a good sign, standing over him now, her face contorted in anger, then she turned and bolted from the room.

The Judge hauled his sorry ass up out of his protective chair and stood. He thought about following Katy back to their bedroom, but he was tired and just not up to it. He wandered into the den, turned Netflix on, and found a scary movie he hoped would hold his attention long enough to forget their incendiary fight. God, but women were unreasonable. He finally went to bed about one-thirty, staying on his side of the bed, noting Katy was riding the edge of her side, keeping as much distance between them as possible.

The next morning the TV alarm went off like clockwork, dumping the Judge into the middle of a re-run of the previous night's documentary newscast on The Strand case. Katy sat up in the bed, tucking her pillows upright behind her to watch, but there was no 'Good Morning' for the Judge, a sign she was still pissed.

The show's anchor, a prominent newscaster, first interviewed Dr. George Gibson, the Director of Minor's Refuge for Change, asking, *"Has any hard evidence been found, such as photographs, animal bones, tunnels, or evidence of Satanic rituals?*

"No," replied Dr. Gibson, *"but medical evidence has proven the abuse took place. Our procedures are not designed to develop evidence, but for diagnosis and treatment."*

"But your procedures are videotaped?"
"Yes."

"And the videotapes will be used by the prosecution in their presentation of this case at the trial?"
"Yes."

The Lead Prosecutor, Jay Armstrong, appeared next, stating, *"The children were molested. We have ample evidence of abuse which will be presented in the courtroom at the appropriate time. Some of the children have experienced sexual irritation, infections, and other things. We even have pictures of the results of the abuse on their young bodies."*

"Couldn't these conditions have occurred as a result of issues unrelated to molestation?"

"Absolutely not."

A parent was interviewed next. *"My two boys, four and five, were molested at the school by two of the faculty. One was forced to play a game called 'Cowboys and Indians', where he had to take his clothes off and let people touch him."*

The show cut to a video of parents raising the branches of a large apple tree in a vacant lot, prodding the ground with sticks under its giant canopy, while other parents examined the ground beneath wild mustard growing across the lot. The voiceover said, *"Parents of the children are still combing the vacant lot and the adjacent areas in this small beach community, looking for further evidence of the devil worship and molestation."*

The show cut to a video of Laura Wilson, escorted from the courtroom into the hall between two bailiffs after the bail hearing. She turned to look directly into the camera, anger flaring across her face, and yelled:

"No evidence of tunnels, photographs, or Satanic rituals will ever be found because none exist. If you want I'll take you to the apple tree where the children claim the Devil lives. You fine upstanding reporters can question the Devil for yourselves."

The Judge laughed, then looked at Katy, who only scowled. The Judge hoisted himself up from the bed and headed for his shower, calling back over his shoulder, "Early morning tomorrow, honey. More work to try to stop this insane witch hunt. And I'll be home late."

172

Katy just sniffed, then submerged herself again beneath the covers.

CHAPTER 27

"Nine new sites, including two local markets and several South Bay residences, were raided this morning by authorities, searching for evidence in The Strand Pre-School investigation. We have it from credible sources that the children say they were taken to the back-storage room of a local market in Ocean Hill and molested on the floor, surrounded by stacks of soda. If that's not disgusting, I don't know what is. This scandal continues to spread across the Southland as frightened parents pull their children out of local pre-schools and seek alternate day-care arrangements."

The Judge rose with a yawn and padded across the floor to switch the TV off, so jaded by now he was almost immune to the daily reports of additional grisly details. The D.A. was grand-standing again. It was said her ratings versus her opponent in the upcoming election were up a solid five points since the Wilsons had been arrested and charged.

Katy had left long before, an early morning at the high school, and they hadn't a chance to talk. He only hoped she'd calmed down. As the Judge finished shaving, his cell phone rang, vibrating itself around the tiled counter in the bathroom in an anguished effort to find the edge and escape to the floor. What had life been like before the damn cell phone? The Judge could hardly remember.

Barney's warm tones came from the cell's speaker: "Just calling to compare notes, Judge. Has your investigation turned up anything new on Jeffrey Simpson's death? The D.A. claims it was murder, even though the autopsy isn't back. She's pushing hard for a murder one charge against both of them if it turns out to have been a homicide. It's going to get ugly if we can't produce an explanation showing it was a note-less suicide, or a live killer if it was a homicide."

"I'm working it, Barney. Lots of leg work. But I'll get to the bottom of it. Have you heard when the autopsy report will be out?"

"Soon."

"Okay, I'm going to explore some more, starting with Jeffrey's current girlfriend. Clair something." The Judge had tracked down her number from Jeffrey's brother, and called to set up a morning appointment. "How's the effort to get a medical expert to testify for our defense?"

Because of the widespread press coverage and the way, the press had tried and convicted the defendants with their ceaseless barrage of information, some factual, some not, it had been difficult to find a practicing doctor willing to testify for the defense.

Barney had finally found an excellent professional, well qualified with tons of experience in identifying child molestation. The expert had reviewed the charts and pictures of scans, the deposition testimony of the prosecution's medical expert, and had declared "the prosecution's medical expert doesn't know what he's talking about. There's no significant evidence of child molestation."

But when the doctor's name was added to the defense's witness list, the newspapers picked it up. The press spread the good doctor's name far and wide, implying the Doc must be desperate for money if he'd agreed to assist this vicious nest of child molesters and testify for the defense.

The poor doctor got calls from his department chair at the university where he taught. He received numerous calls from his colleagues warning him to back off. He got calls from the Los Angeles D.A.'s office and the California Attorney General's office, applying not-so-subtle pressure. The clincher was a call from the foundation funding his research. The Foundation made it clear they didn't want to be associated with a doctor who'd wade into the The Strand Pre-School case and testify for the defense. He immediately caved and withdrew as an expert witness despite Barney's pleas to remain..

This had precipitated a frantic ongoing search by Barney for a qualified doctor who could rebut the D.A.'s anticipated medical testimony. So far there were no takers. The case was just too hot.

As the Judge bounded down the steps to his garage and his car, he wondered what Simpson's current girlfriend would be like. He supposed she wasn't the 'current' girlfriend, since Jeffrey was dead. She must be distraught. To be so close to someone, and then one day the special someone just up and kills himself. It must be very traumatic.

Clair Henderson lived with a roommate in a small ramshackle house in North Ocean Hill. The place was considerably uphill from the beach, a postage-stamp cottage built early in the last century. All wood shingles painted a New England blue, with white trim.

The Judge strolled across a dead lawn, now romantically called 'golden brown' by Angelinos, or alternatively, 'going for the Gold' to put a best face on the continuing Southern California drought. The yard was framed on both sides by a white picket fence. He stepped onto a white wood porch that creaked and threatened to give way under his feet. He suspected it was held together by termites. He rapped on the knocker, which was nailed onto the yellow door set in the middle of all the blue siding. Cub-Scout colors, mused the Judge.

Nothing happened. So, he rapped again. The door suddenly flew open. He stared down at a petite young woman in cutoff jeans and a low-cut top, late twenties. She had large boobs, cantilevered out from her body, apparently permanently destined to remain airborne as the result of straps and supports, seen and unseen. He wondered if it took two to unhook things. It must be dangerous for her in any sort of wind.

She had long blond hair, large brown eyes, and a direct smile that cheered. Nice legs too below the cutoffs, smooth and tan, towering over bright pink toenails on small feet. She was a pretty girl and she knew it. He wondered how Jeffrey had gotten so lucky. And why anyone would want to check out when he had a babe like this in his bed.

She paused a few seconds, looking up at his six feet, throwing her shoulders back and thrusting her chest forward, allowing him a generous look. Then she stuck out a small paw, also with pink nails.

"You must be the Judge."

He took the petite hand extended, careful so as not to damage it in his meaty grip and muttered. "Yes, ma'am. That's me. And you must be Clair."

He felt awkward and he didn't know why. Clair assessed him with almost professional interest. She didn't look the grieving girlfriend he was expecting.

She flounced him into a tiny living room and nested on one end of a faded red sofa, patting with her hand for him to sit down beside her, close beside her since it was a very small sofa, almost a loveseat.

"Thanks for speaking to me, Clair. As I said on the phone, I'm not with the police. I represent Laura Wilson. I'm trying to find out what happened to Jeffrey. Any perspective you could give on his state of mind and any enemies he might have would be greatly appreciated."

"You think maybe he didn't kill himself?" Clair's eyes went wide as she digested the Judge's words.

"That's what I'm trying to determine, Clair. That's why I called. You were his girlfriend?"

"How do you mean?"

"I was told by his brother that you and Jeffrey were an item. You know, going together."

"That's not absolutely correct."

"Oh. Tell me what's correct."

"Well, I have lots of boyfriends."

"Lots?"

"Yes. Well I mean I'm not an escort or anything, but I like men, and men like me, so I always have two or three guys, you know, to have fun with."

"To be intimate with?" The question just popped out. The Judge was curious now.

"That's a pretty personal question, Judge. Shame on you." But she said it with a big smile and rolled her baby browns in a little girl way that was very charming. Very, very charming.

The Judge sat a little straighter on the love seat. The trouble with being an old fart, he mused, was that you never thought you were an old fart. You always saw yourself as that late twenty-something young man and ignored the ravages of time. Ah well. It was fun to fantasize.

"I don't like to characterize my life like that, Judge." Clair was rattling on now. "Let's say I have a significant relationship with each of my men. You know, love, sex, these are natural things. It's how we're all built. It's very normal to want sex with a lover, to spend time with him, to make him happy with your body. To be tight together. It's how the human race evolved. If you're going to do it with one, it's as easy to do it with three."

"So, you and Jeffrey weren't exclusive?"

"No."

"Do these guys give you money?"

"Another personal question. Wow. No foreplay for you!" Another big smile; kind of a hello, not a goodbye, thought the Judge.

"Sorry. I'm just trying to assess where Jeffrey was in his life, how he was, whether he might want to take his life. But tell me more about your relationships."

"Well, my male friends take me out. Show me a good time. And yes, I receive an expense allowance to cover my clothes and makeup and stuff, so I look good for each guy. It takes a lot of time and its costs money to kit a girl out proper so she's attractive. And the older a girl gets, the more time and the more money required. Depressing, huh?"

"You look great to me, Clair." The Judge clanged his jaws shut, mentally slapping himself the side of the head for uttering what he was thinking. "Do you work at a job?"

"I go to school. But Judge, really, this other thing is also my job. That's what I'm trying to tell you. Now suppose we went out, you and me. We'd have a great time I'm sure. Fancy dinners, perhaps some travel. I'd listen to all your lawyer war stories, fascinating. You'd get all this attention, I'd rub your shoulders, make you relaxed, release all your tension. You know, the way a woman can. And you'd want to give me an allowance each month, wouldn't you, to cover some of my expenses."

"Well, I…"

"Of course you would. Not much. Perhaps fifteen hundred as an expense allowance to start. And we'd have such an awfully good time."

"But did Jeffrey have money to give you an expense allowance?"

"Not at first. He was really cute, and he made some big promises, but then he didn't come through."

"Oh."

"That was a problem. He didn't have money very often. I liked him a lot, but he really couldn't afford to take care of me. A girl has to be selective, has to have rules, follow them. My mother use to say, 'No ticky... no laundry.'"

"Yes, of course."

"But then... but then, Judge. Jeffrey suddenly came through big time. He was swimming in money and we had such a wonderful time."

"Do you know where he got the money?"

"I think he closed a big deal or something. I'm not sure. He said he was in distribution."

"Did Jeffrey know you weren't exclusive?"

"We never talked about it. Guys always want to think I'm private stock. I find it's easier if we don't discuss it. For instance, if you and I started something. it would be very discreet, Judge, and just for you. I suspect you're married. Older married guys are my favorite: reliable, sweet, and dry, like a plant that hasn't been watered for a while." The Judge got the batting brown eyes again along with a radiant smile. It made him think of Marylyn Monroe.

"But, if you think about it, Judge, just one friend doesn't pay the rent, particularly in this town. You need two or three."

"So, neither of your other two friends knew about Jeffrey?"

"Well, officially no. But Jackson, that's his first name, he's the one's paying me three grand a month, kind of got suspicious."

"How do you know?"

"He started asking me a lot of questions, and then last time I left his penthouse in Hollywood in the morning, I think someone followed me."

"Was he angry?"

"Boy, I'll say, and it was just a suspicion. It's not like he caught me in flagrante delicto or something."

"You know Latin?"

"I'm going for my master's degree in literature, Judge. I'm not just another pretty face. Anyway, Jackson's a scary dude, tied up in business with the Chicago mob. I'm careful not to discuss his business with him. I don't want to know."

"If he'd found out about Jeffrey, what do you think he'd have done?"

"Oh, Shit. He'd have killed Jeffrey, killed my roommate, locked me up somewhere in the desert. I'd be toast."

"But Jackson didn't find out?"

"No."

"Are you sure?"

"Well, no. But he hasn't said anything, or slapped me around, so I think its safe.

"How often did you and Jeffrey meet?"

"Well that was another problem. Jeffrey spent a lot of time on his job at that pre-school. He even had to work nights sometimes. Suddenly he was flush with cash but had not so much time for fun with me."

"Often that's how it works, Clair."

"Course I didn't mind 'cause I needed to see my other guy friends too. Spread myself around, you know. I've learned not to be too dependent on any one guy. Look at what's happened now. It's a clear example.

Suddenly no more Jeffrey. If I were dependent solely on him, I'd be screwed… Or, I guess I wouldn't be… but I'd be broke."

The Judge got the full smile again, this time with teeth.

"When was the last time you saw Jeffrey?"

"The night before he died."

"Did he seem depressed?"

"No. He seemed his usual self."

"Not a little tense, nervous, maybe stressed?"

"Come to think of it he was a little stressed. Didn't sleep well. Had some trouble with Big John. Getting him up." She chuckled.

"Do you think he killed himself?"

"Just assumed so. It's what the papers say."

"Was he in trouble with anyone? "

"There was someone he was concerned about."

"Who?"

"Don't know. But he said he'd had a falling out a couple of weeks before with this guy, a sort of business partner. He said not to tell anyone where he worked."

"A guy? Not a woman?"

"That's my impression. Not competition with me. Of course there's no such thing as competition where I'm concerned." Clair leaned a little closer to the Judge.

"And Jeffrey was worried?"

"I don't know that 'worried' is right. He said it was something he could handle."

"Do you know what kind of business Jeffrey was involved in?"

"No."

"But you said he'd recently come into some money?"

"Yes."

"A lot of money?"

"When he opened his wallet he kind of flashed around the wad of hundreds in there. He maybe had five grand on him last time we went out."

"Where'd you go?"

"He picked me up here. We went out to Shades for drinks, dinner, watched the sun set over Redondo Harbor. Then we came back here and settled in. Tried to mess around a little, watched some TV, tried to mess around some more. But no happy ending for Jeffrey. So, we went to sleep."

"He stayed over."

"He did."

"You going to miss him?"

"Of course. He was a friend, and a benefactor. But life goes on, Judge. It's like my mom use to say, 'The dog barks... but the caravan moves on.'"

CHAPTER 28

Right on cue, the TV blasted away at seven a.m. the next morning.

"Hermosa Beach Counselman Jack Webber, speaking for a parent group against child abuse, has announced a ten-thousand-dollar reward for pornographic photos of The Strand Pre-School children, either nude or engaging in sex acts. Counselman Webber stated, 'We know the photos are out there and we need your help to find them.' This scandal continues to grow, day by day, people. The D.A. says she's prepared to file one hundred additional charges of child abuse, and now says she has forty-two confirmed child victims, and investigations running on more than thirty additional perpetrators."

"Damn," muttered the Judge. He had meant to turn the TV's alarm feature off the night before. The news was depressing. But at least no one had found incriminating photographs. He believed they wouldn't.

The Judge climbed from his bed and consulted his calendar. He'd made an appointment to see Jeffrey Simpson's mother, Elaine Simpson, this morning. He stood there a moment staring out at the Bay, wondering what really happened in that maintenance room at The Strand Pre-School that night.

Jeffrey Simpson's mother lived by herself in a small bungalow in Northern Torrance, affectionately called Old Torrance by the locals. The Judge pulled up in front of a Spanish Stucco from the Forties, whitewashed walls, peeling blue paint on the trim, rusting black iron fencing around a tiled front patio entered through a rickety garden gate. On the other side was a raised front porch with an old wooden door of Spanish design. He walked to the door and rang the bell.

Immediately steps shuffled across the floor in the interior, and then the front door opened just enough for the Judge to slide through if he turned sideways, which he did. He entered a dark entry hall of brown polished floors and beige walls.

Elaine Simpson, early seventies, was tall, but stood bent and hunched in her black skirt and matching black silk blouse. She had straight wispy white hair, framing a lean face lathered with wrinkles. Pale green eyes focused on the Judge unblinkingly out of dark circles as though measuring prey, the dark circles suggesting a lack of sleep. Her peaky nose disturbed an otherwise symmetrical face, pale and white, giving her the aspect of a hawk when she turned sideways.

She invited the Judge into her modest living room, cheap Ikea furniture, a faded wedding picture over the fireplace, and a lone picture of her eldest son, Erwin, much younger, no racoon eyes, on a distressed coffee table.

She offered tea, then disappeared into the kitchen and bustled out with a laden tray. There was a yellow china teapot displaying Japanese sketches in black ink, chipped a little around the spout but obviously loved, matching yellow tea cups for two, a plate of peanut butter cookies, and a small blue bottle, no label, filled with clear fluid.

She prepared the tea with ceremony, apparently a calming ritual, and offered the Judge a cup, which he accepted. She pointed to the mysterious blue bottle. "Gin?"

The Judge shook his head.

She lavished her tea with a healthy dollop and sipped, waiting, expectantly for the Judge's next move.

"As we discussed, I'm here to talk about Jeffrey. I'm investigating what happened. And as I said, I represent Laura Wilson."

Her nose crinkled up for an instant at the mention of Laura's name, as though she'd caught a whiff of rotten eggs.

"Do you believe Jeffrey committed suicide?"

Pale blue eyes, watery now, continued to pin the Judge's. There was a long silence. Finally, she spoke, carefully, with a hint of anger.

"It doesn't surprise me, Judge. Jeff was a small runt of a boy, and not much more as a man, not like his older brother, Erwin." There was a bitterness in her voice now. "Jeff was always trouble for me. Always bullied in school. Always failing his classes. Always cutting classes. One year he tried shoplifting. That cost me a pretty penny in lawyers. I wanted him to grow up like Erwin, make something of himself, be proud of him. But it wasn't in his nature. Did you know Erwin sends me money every month? To help. All Jeff did was drain cash."

"But he went into the Army, fought in Afghanistan."

"Yes. I talked him into that. Thought it might make him into a man. He screwed that up too. Came back with his PTSD bullshit, whining around me,

187

around that bitch of a wife he married, around his brother, anyone who'd listen. Even had the doctor from the VA hospital came out to the beach to listen to his sad tale. He was meeting the doc twice a month over in Westwood. My son was a whiner."

"And you believe he was capable of suicide?"

Jeff was never a happy person. So yes. I can believe he committed suicide. He's often been very depressed."

"Do you think Jeffrey was sad? Or did it go beyond that, into despair? Did Jeffrey say things like 'I have no reason to live,' 'I have no future worth living,' 'I'm helpless and powerless to stop my pain,' 'My life is meaningless," or similar things? Did you sense that Jeffrey felt hopeless, useless, purposeless?"

"Well, Judge, Jeff certainly was useless, couldn't even help me out a little, like his older brother does, with my rent and stuff. And if you ask me Jeff was pretty much aimless, going from one tinker toy job to another. Like that maintenance job at the pre-school. Never trying to make something of himself. I'm only surprised he had the guts to go through with a suicide. Must have been desperate. Likely out of money for his drugs."

"I understand he was living with his brother, Erwin, some."

"He was until their big fight."

"They had a fight?"

"Erwin kicked him out. Erwin said Jeff stole money from him, probably for drugs. Erwin was incensed. Threw Jeff out on his ear about four weeks ago. I guess Jeff moved in full time at the pre-school after that. He had a cot or something there. But I wasn't surprised. That was Jeff, always trouble."

"Where's Jeffrey's dad?"

"Long gone. A teamster. Made good money when he worked, but a party boy and a letch. Ran around on me, drank himself into an early grave. Served him right. Erwin was eighteen, Jeff was twelve when he died, cirrhosis of the liver. Erwin took it hard."

"And Jeff?"

"Didn't give a shit."

"Was there any insurance on Jeffrey's life?"

Elaine Simpson tensed, sitting up straighter, eyes narrowing, caution spreading across her face.

"Yeah. A small policy."

"How small?"

"I don't think that's any of your business."

"Was his ex-wife the beneficiary?"

"Not on this one. I'm the beneficiary."

"Oh."

"Took it out myself after Jeff came back from the army. I could see he was running himself into the ground. I wasn't ever going to get repaid all the money I loaned him. Made him take a physical, sign the docs, make me the recipient of the money."

"Was it a fifty-thousand-dollar policy?" asked the Judge.

"Oh no, Judge. Oh no. Much, much more." Simpson gave him a sly smile. "I'm not saying nothing more about that."

"Did Jeffrey speak Spanish?"

"No."

"You're sure?"

"Yes. Why do you ask?"

"Just a thought. What's the story on his dog?"

"Frosty? A mean little dog. Hated me and I hated it. Jeff dragged it around with him wherever he could, made us put up with its nasty little habits. Peed on my rug, dug up my tulip garden, bit the mailman. Someone hit it in the street. Good riddance I say."

"Was Jeffrey upset when the dog got hit?"

"Yeah, for a day or two. Tried to con money out of me for a funeral. I told him where he could stick that idea."

"So, he was upset?"

"Maybe. Or maybe he was just out of drug money again; any excuse would do with him. I don't think he gave a rat's ass about the dog after it ate the concrete."

"So, loss of the dog wouldn't be a reason for Jeffrey to perhaps commit suicide?"

Ms. Simpson cackled at that thought. It was a mean cackle.

"You didn't approve of his job at The Strand?"

"I didn't say that."

"You referred to Jeffrey's job as a tinker toy job."

"I was surprised when he got the job. Jeff hardly ever accomplished anything by himself."

"Did Jeffrey ever talk about what went on at the pre-school?"

"You mean those people screwing up those kids, taking dirty pictures and stuff?"

"Yes."

"No. I found out about it like everybody else, in the newspapers."

"You think it really happened, Ms. Simpson?"

"That child abuse stuff? Could have. I'd believe it of that Laura Wilson. She's a conniving bitch with a wet appetite and no self-restraint. But no, Jeff never talked about it."

"The police believe Jeffrey was coming into their station the next day, the day after his death, to give evidence about child molestation going on at the school."

"Maybe he was, I don't know. But Jeff never did anything for anyone unless it benefited Jeff. Maybe he was blackmailing her."

"Who?'

"Laura Wilson."

"You don't think much of Laura Wilson."

"Not after the way she treated my son."

"You heard she was letting him go from the school maintenance job?"

"That, and I didn't like that they were screwing."

"Who?"

"Jeff and that Laura woman."

The Judge sat back, stunned, feeling color rising in his face, trying hard to mask his shock.

"You believe Jeffrey and Laura Wilson were lovers?"

"You didn't know? Don't know your client very well, do you Judge?" Simpson cackled again. "Crap, she was ten years Jeff's senior, should have left my boy be. Jeff really got involved, said he loved her, wanted to make it the real deal."

The Judge was suddenly taken back to the maintenance room, looking at the cot made up as a daybed, the bedding all violet and flowers, not something a man would choose. It was a woman's touch. Laura's touch. He should have seen it right off. The lady with the inexhaustible sexual appetite. He remembered it well.

No wonder Harry Wilson was so angry about Simpson. The little room was their love nest. Laura was the secret girlfriend. The one Jeffrey had a falling out with, the one who broke Jeffrey's heart.

"Why did Laura dump Jeffrey?"

"Jeff said sometimes he couldn't get it up."

Yes. That even sounded like Laura. She wouldn't put up with nonperformance for long. In that department she was very needy.

"Jeff let the affair slip out when we were talking, so he told me the whole sordid story."

"How long?"

"Not sure. But she just dumped him, used him, then dumped him." Simpson snapped her fingers. "Just like that."

"So maybe that's why he hung himself." The Judge said in a muffled voice.

"That might be it, Judge. It's her type. A sexual predator, if you ask me." Simpson folded her arms, signifying her opinion on Laura Wilson was closed.

"How'd Jeffrey take being… dumped?"

"How do you think? He was distraught. Jeff said the Wilson Witch was so physically demanding no guy could keep up. Said he petered out early the last couple of times, and… boom… he's fired. She's a cold bitch."

"This was just before he died?"

"Yes. I spoke to Jeff the afternoon before."

"He say anything else?"

"Well, yeah. We hadn't spoken for perhaps three weeks. He said he'd come into a lot of money."

"He say where it came from?"

"No. Maybe Jeff got your little Miss Laura to pay him off for being silent about their affair."

"It sounds like they were two single consenting adults."

"Oh, come, come, Judge. Can you image the headlines? *Local Pre-School Principle Screwing the Handyman While Young Children Entrusted to Her Care Languish.* Think of all the 'tool' jokes it'd stimulate, and perhaps a few toolbelt jokes as well. The Strand would have been toast. Bet she'd have paid a pretty penny to keep that quiet."

"Would Jeffrey do something like that?"

"Jeff was Jeff. My son was on drugs. He'd do anything for money. Maybe Laura Wilson killed my son and made it look like a suicide."

CHAPTER 29

The next morning the Judge awoke with a start, having overslept. He had an appointment to meet with Barney and their two clients at the L.A. Jail at nine a.m. He felt anxious and angry but wasn't sure why. Then he remembered. Laura had lied to him.

He made a dive for the bathroom and its shower, tripping over Annie the Dog sprawled in the bathroom doorway. He snarled, "Get out of the damn way," using his raspy voice from his days on the bench. The poor animal leaped up from a sound nap and dashed for cover under the table in the dining room, turning to peer out with hurt eyes, worried she'd committed some unforgivable sin. "Served her right," he muttered to himself.

Katy was having breakfast in the breakfast room as he dashed past, heading for the front door and the garage.

"Do you want some toast and coffee, Judge?"

"No." he muttered, scowling at her.

"Whoa, someone's in a good mood this morning. What happened, did you leave your sense of humor in the bed?"

"I think I left my innocence there, Katy. See you tonight." He stormed out the door, down to the garage, and roared away in his Mercedes Convertible.

Barney, Harry Wilson and Laura Wilson were huddled around a table in a small room, grey walls, grey linoleum floors, and one small window high up which threw little light, hardly competition for the fluorescent light fixture in the ceiling casting it sterile light down on the room's occupants.

Barney's face broke into a big smile. "Judge, we were just waiting for you. Pull up a chair and we can get started."

"No," snapped the Judge. "Laura." The Judge waved an accusing index finger at her. "We need to talk. Now! Privately."

Laura slowly rose from her chair, worry spreading across her face. Barney and Harry's jaws dropped.

"This way," the Judge muttered briskly, leading her out the metal door into the hands of the waiting sheriff's deputy who showed them to a separate room, identical to the first. Laura collapsed into one of the mean little plastic chairs, fear in her eyes.

"You lied to me, Laura," thundered the Judge, electing to stand and pace back and forth in front of her. "You lied." He could feel his face getting red, his blood pressure raising.

"What are you talking about, Judge? What have I done?"

"What have you done? You didn't think it might be relevant that you were sleeping with Jeffrey Simpson? Sleeping with him at your own school? With the children a few feet away? Enjoying sexual escapades in the afternoon while your brother tried to keep the school running?"

"Oh. That. Well... no, I guess I didn't think it was relevant." Laura's face showed confusion now.

"You know how I am Judge. You know better than anybody. When I have an itch, well, I have to scratch."

"And when Jeffrey couldn't scratch satisfactorily anymore, you dumped him as a lover, fired him as your maintenance man, turned your back on him. Left him to twist in the wind."

"It wasn't like that, Judge. It was always just a fling. Neither of us took it as anything serious. When it was over, well, it was over. And it was time for him to go. He understood that."

"Did he?"

"Yes."

"Not according to his mother, and his brother. They say he was deeply hurt, distraught even, at being dumped. Apparently, he thought it was the real thing with you, real love."

Laura cast her eyes down on the table, quiet for a moment. Then she looked up at the Judge, tears in her eyes. "I was very fond of the little guy, Judge. And when he was hot, he was really hot. But he was drug ridden, in serious trouble with somebody, running scared, hiding out at my school. I needed him out of there for the sake of The Strand and for the sake of my own sanity.

Somehow, about four weeks before his death, he came into a lot of money, I don't know where or why, but it was a lot. Over fifty Gs, I think. So, he didn't need the job anymore, he didn't need my financial support anymore, and he didn't need me. I feared what he might be involved in. I needed him out of my school and I took the opportunity of his good fortune to negotiate his termination. He was okay with leaving. He understood."

"Did you kill him, Laura?"

"Judge! No. No, I didn't kill him. I would never do something like that. How could I have hoisted him up on the beam?"

"We both know you're buff, strong, coordinated. And with your firefighter training it wouldn't have been hard."

"Judge... You're wrong. Just wrong."

"Did he threaten to go public about your little afternoon love nest?"

"No."

"Were you molesting children, and he knew about it? Was he going to go spill what he knew to the Ocean Hill Police the next day?"

"No, Judge. No. It was nothing like that."

"Then why didn't you tell me about him?"

"I... I figured you might get jealous, might jump ship, abandon me. I... I couldn't take the chance."

"Did your brother know?"

"I don't know. I think he suspected."

"What a mess. What a fuckin' mess. Don't you see, if the autopsy shows Simpson was murdered, and if he was alive with you, if you were the last person to see him alive, then you're the natural target for the police investigation. You, and probably Harry, too."

"But I didn't kill Jeffrey, Judge."

"You had opportunity and access. You had motives, first to stop him from going to the Ocean Hill police, and second to stop him from broadcasting how he was sleeping with you afternoons at The Strand. Where were you that night?"

"The night he hung himself?"

197

"Yes."

"I was at home, at my flat, watching Netflix."

"By yourself?"

"Yes."

"So, you have no alibi, Laura."

"No. Oh, Judge, what am I going to do? I'm so, so sorry."

"We'll figure it out. For now, I don't want you discussing anything about Jeffrey Simpson, or your relationship with him, with either Barney or your brother. Got it?"

"Yes. But why?"

"Because once the D.A. gets wind of this, and assuming Jeffrey's death was a homicide, either or both of you may be charged with murder. There could be a joint trial or separate trials. You'll each need separate counsel. And it's unlikely you'll want to undertake a coordinated defense with your brother. I don't want you saying anything that may come back to haunt you later."

"Oh my God, Judge," Laura gasped, then put her head in her hands and began to softly cry.

CHAPTER 30

"The parents of at least fifty children thought to have been abused at The Strand Pre-School have banded together to form a website and an organization under the name Me Too Parents.

Lists of people suspected of participating in the alleged Satanic ring, and those who looked the other way and facilitated the ring's existence and its sexual exploitation of the children, are being posted on the site, on a page entitled The Wall of Shame.

This morning, someone put up the name of a local retired judge who resides in Palos Verdes and is said to be helping the Wilsons wriggle out of the grievous charges brought against them.

There is still…"

The Judge made a dive for the TV from his bed, shutting the newscaster off in mid-sentence, but it was too late. Katy was standing in the doorway to the bathroom, dripping around the edges of the red towel wrapped around her. She'd heard it all. Her face crumpled into a mask of agony and disbelief as she swung to face the Judge, her index finger on her right hand straightening out from what had been a fist, pointing a silent accusation at the Judge's face with all the fury of a defending mother.

"You… you… you've allowed this to happen, Judge. You've ruined our lives, yours, mine, Ralphie's. People will never forget or forgive."

She spun back into the bathroom, slamming the door with a force that rattled every window in the house. Annie the Dog came running, partly at the noise, partly at the quality of hurt in Katy's voice, giving the Judge one disdainful glance, then settling in front of the bathroom door, preventing unwanted intrusion from anyone.

Things were slammed down and around in anger in the bathroom, then there was the sound of porcelain breaking, as though someone had lifted the top of the toilet and flung it on to the floor. After that it went quiet for a while.

Katy emerged finally emerged, fully dressed, cold, aloof, stepping over Annie the Dog, marching out toward the living room. Annie got up and formally followed Katy out, nose in the air, tail arched in a rigid circle. The Judge heard the front door slam. Katy was off to work.

Later in the morning Barney and the Judge huddled in a small conference room at the courthouse reserved for attorneys, to lay plans for the *voir dire* of the jury. *Voir dire*, French for 'to speak the truth,' was the process of questioning potential jurors drawn from the jury pool to determine their competence and suitability to serve on the jury panel at a trial.

"This is a nasty situation, Judge. With all this negative news coverage, how can we possibly get an impartial jury? Even if we move to another county in California, this case is in the press all over the U.S. Our clients have been tried and convicted by the press before we even start."

"I have to believe the system will work better than that, Barney. Let's do the best job we can to ask the right questions and get the questionable people off the jury panel. And have faith the remaining jurors will listen with an open mind."

"All right. I have a good list of questions we can use to smoke out prejudice and bias." Said Barney.

"Why don't we ask each juror what he thinks his verdict might be?" said the Judge.

"I wish Judge. But you know full well Judge Ferguson isn't going to let us ask a juror to pre-judge our case, or ask the juror to suggest what their verdict might be at the outset."

"That's the legal rule, Barney. But sometimes there's a way to ask just such an inappropriate question and the Judge won't jump on us. We just have to be clever about it."

"I'm all ears, Judge. How do we do that?"

"Most judges will allow us to quietly ask jurors to pre-judge individual facts and issues in the case, Barney, as long as we either re-frame the questions to ask the jurors about their own personal approaches and experiences, or we generalize the questions so we're not directly asking about our defendants."

"I knew you were a clever bastard, Judge, but sometimes you still surprise me. What do you have in mind?"

"Well, if we just feed the key facts of our case to potential jurors and ask them, 'based on those facts, do you think the defendants are guilty?', we'll draw a sustained objection from Armstrong, and Ferguson will have a cow."

"I agree."

"But consider this, Barney. By now the prospective jurors have already heard about the case and what it's about, particularly given the lavish press coverage. And even though Ferguson will tell the jurors that what they've heard about the case in the press and elsewhere is not evidence, jurors don't understand the distinction. From a juror's perspective, he's already heard facts and evidence and made some pre-judgements. So, we simply need to frame our questions around the premise that any pre-judging by a juror is an inappropriate bias."

"What do you think we can get away with?"

"We can ask questions like, 'Based on what you've heard so far, even though it's not evidence, do you already feel like the defendants have done something wrong?'"

"I get it, Judge. We're asking jurors to pre-judge under the cover of trying to identify jurors who can't follow the rules."

"There's an even more creative way to ask a juror to directly comment on the worst fact in our case."

"Which fact is our worst do you think, Judge?"

"The testimony of the children."

Barney nodded.

The Judge continued, "I propose this question: 'As you've likely heard, Mr. Prospective Juror, there are several children who are going to say they were molested by the defendants. Will this fact alone, that these children say, for whatever reason and no matter how they have been pre-programmed, that they were molested by the defendants, automatically cause you to disregard the other evidence in this case, or disregard the law as it applies in this case?'":

"Shit, Judge, clever. Ferguson will see that as looking for jurors who won't follow jury instructions because they already have an unqualified opinion as to the merits based on their knowledge from the press."

"You've got it Barney. Ninety percent of the time a judge will let this sort of question fly."

"And you've really asked them what verdict they're predisposed to give."

"Yes."

"Okay, I'll work up questions around your suggestions and we'll see if we can get the Wilsons an untainted jury. But Judge, our other problem just got a lot bigger."

"What now?"

"My buddy at the coroner's office called this morning."

"And?"

"Homicide. Jeffrey Simpson was murdered."

"Shit."

"You're right, Judge, that's exactly what it is, and we're up to our eyeballs."

"How'd he die? Did someone tie his hands and hoist him up there?"

"Half right. Uncertain whether someone tied his hands. But there was a small needle mark on his neck. It was some sort of Succinylcholine compound, apparently. It's used in surgeries. Someone shot him up with that stuff, paralyzed him so he couldn't move a muscle. He was conscious but helpless while the belt was put around his neck. And he was lifted up on that stool and the belt was looped around the pipe and beam while he helplessly watched. Then someone

Davis MacDonald

kicked the stool away and that was that. Miserable way to go."

"So, it couldn't have been Laura Wilson," said the Judge, hopeful Barney would buy his argument. "How could she lift a dead weight like Jeffrey up on the stool, and then stabilize him there while she put the belt around his neck?"

"That's not what the police say. They say she's a firefighter, trained to do exactly that sort of shit. Besides, they say, Jeffrey was a small man, and Laura is a big strapping girl and very fit. She's built like an Amazon, Judge, anyone can see that. Including jurors."

The Judge swore. "The police think she did it?"

"They're investigating. They think either her alone, or her and her brother."

"With what motive?"

"You know the answer to that, Judge. Jeffrey was going to spill the beans on The Strand Pre-School molestation ring to the police the very next day."

"Crap, Barney, we don't need this."

Barney gave the Judge a searching look, and asked quietly, "Do you think Laura killed Jeffrey, Judge?"

"I can't believe she'd do something like that."

"Christ, well you better find out who did, and in a hurry, Judge."

"I'm working on it."

"Work faster."

CHAPTER 31

It was morning. There was talking in his head.
Shit. No. It wasn't just in his head. It was the damn
TV... again. He listened.

*"More shocking news on The Strand Pre-School case.
There's a neighboring pre-school, located in Torrance, called the
Good Fun Pre-School. What a name for a pre-school, huh?
We're told the Good Fun Pre-School has been trading children
with The Strand Pre-School for molestation fun and games for
years.*

*A parent has come forward to tell a sordid story of
how her child was sent home from the Good Fun Pre-School with
just outer clothes, carrying her underwear in a bag. For God
sakes, what's going on in this country?*

*We spoke to the little girl's teacher. His explanation
was hardly satisfactory. Here's that video clip."*

The Judge rolled over to watch. The video was
of a nice-looking man, late twenties, sandy complexion,
a mic thrust under his nose, very earnest and totally
naive.

*"Did you send your class home without underwear last
month, Mr. Larkin?"*

"They had underwear."

"But were they wearing their underwear?"

*"Well... no. But they all took their underwear home
with them. Nobody lost underwear."*

"*That's hardly the point, is it? What was going on that they were running around at your school without underwear?*"

"*Oh, I see. Well... see... their underwear got wet. It was a very hot day. I told them they could take off their outer clothes and run through the sprinklers in their underwear. It's their favorite sort of play you know?*"

"*And their underwear got wet?*"

"*Yes. And I was... surprised, you know... how wet it got. So, our female teacher had the girls and I had the boys take their wet underwear off and put them in plastic bags, and just put their outer clothes back on. So, they all went home with their wet underwear in plastic bags. No one lost any underwear.*"
The young man produced a big smile, having settled the issue.

The screen returned to the commentator.

"*Give me a break. Do you really believe that was all that was going on? The California Department of Social Services has ordered the Good Fun Pre-School closed pending a review of their license and facilities, and an investigation of whether there were unauthorized day trips of their young charges between the Good Fun Pre-School and The Strand.*

Meanwhile, prosecutors in the Wilson case say they now have over three hundred nine children from The Strand Pre-School who have 'admitted' they were molested at that school."

The Judge groaned as he used the remote to shut the TV off. Annie the Dog came running in to see what the trouble was, thinking he was in pain. Well, shit, he was, damn it. This case was driving him nuts.

Katy was already gone with Ralphie who was being dropped off at a new pre-school Katy had chosen. Probably the Good Fun Pre-School, the Judge mused sourly. He showered, shaved and headed out of the house, checking the small calendar that lived in his pocket. He was disdainful of the online calendars everyone else seemed to use. He had an appointment with the VA doctor Jeffrey Simpson had been seeing.

The VA Hospital in West L.A. was a structure designed with an eye to the Transformer movies:, seven stories high in long lines, with square pilings driven into the earth periodically. It was horizontal, rectangular, squat and forbidding. Its saving grace was its large surrounding campus, park-like in size, and its location in West L.A., anchoring the 405 Freeway to the west and Wilshire Boulevard to the south, a stone's throw from UCLA.

The Judge pulled his Mercedes into the parking lot and meandered around lines of parked cars until he found a suitable end spot toward the back, not a compact. He swung in close to the curb on the passenger side, reducing the risk of his door being dinged. It was ten a.m., a warm sunny day, and it gave him pleasure to stretch his legs, walking the length of the lot to reach the steps leading to the main entrance.

He punched the elevator button to the third floor, Psychosocial Services, and stepped out, almost bumping into Sam Reynolds, Jeffrey's army buddy, who had been making a dive to catch the elevator doors. Sam missed it and muttered, "Fuck" under his breath.

"Hi, Sam. Remember me?"

Sam Reynolds' face filled with recognition, his meaty hand shooting out and wrapping around the Judge's hand to give a bone-crushing shake.

"Nice to see you again, Judge. Just picking up some meds. You figure out why my old buddy killed himself yet?"

The Judge shook his head. "There's something you should know. Jeffrey didn't kill himself."

"Holy Shit. Someone killed him? For God sakes. Why?"

"I'm not sure. But I'm going to find out. Is Doctor Stevens your doctor here?"

"Yes. He's a good guy. It helps me a lot to see him. But I'm running late now. Call me if you have more questions about Jeff. I'll help any way I can." Reynolds made another dive for a second closing elevator door, this time catching it and disappearing inside.

The Judge stepped into the middle of a large waiting area, or perhaps holding tank was a better description. Thirty vets waited, most looking hang-dog dispirited, seated in uncomfortable ancient metal chairs, or just on the floor, their backs to the battleship grey walls. The Judge marched over to a grim looking nurse manning a beat-up desk across the room, and declared he had an appointment with Dr. Stevens. She appraised him with steely grey eyes behind steel rimmed glasses, then picked up her phone and whispered into it, listened for a moment, then pointed with her thumb to the long hall to her right, muttering, "Room Three-Oh-Eight."

Dr. Stevens turned out to be an old guy, older than the Judge even, early sixties, dressed in jeans and a blue-striped short-sleeve shirt under his de rigueur white coat. He looked very collegian, despite the stubble of short cut grey hair on top of his head, heavily receded at the sides, and the hint of white stubble across his chin and the sides of his jaw. He had light brown eyes, flanked by lots of lines which stretched up to his forehead and down across his cheeks. The kind the Judge had seen on alcoholics and druggies. A recovered user perhaps.

"Thanks for seeing me, Doctor." The Judge stuck out a hand and produced his best boyish smile, hoping this would thaw out some information that wouldn't normally be given. "As I said in our telephone conversation, I'm one of the defense attorneys in The Strand-Pre-School case."

"Yes, well, I don't know how that relates to Jeffrey Simpson. I've only got ten minutes to talk. And the police have already been here."

"I know. But you agreed a short meeting here and now could be useful to the defense, and might avoid a lengthy deposition for you downtown later."

"Yes. Okay. Go ahead."

"You know how Mr. Simpson was found."

"Yes. Most unfortunate. Can't say I saw that coming. But you never know with these vets. It's so tragic. They come back with wounds no one can see. Sometimes they just shrink into themselves, collapsing ever further, until there's nothing left."

"Is that what happened with Jeffrey?"

"I don't know. I've reviewed my notes. He seemed to be progressing. His bouts of depression were decreasing in frequency and length. The medication seemed to help. He said he was sleeping better. But you can never be sure what they tell you is true."

"Did Jeffrey have any friends here? Other patients, maybe in a support group or something?"

"That would be part of his confidential records."

"But he's dead."

"I know. But I can't ethically breach the doctor's covenant of confidentiality."

"Unless there's a court order."

"Unless there's a court order."

"So, you can't tell me the nature of his depression?"

"No."

"Something to do with his time overseas in the army, PTSD perhaps?"

"I can't comment."

"What medication was he on?"

"I can't give you that information."

"Was it an opioid, perhaps OxyContin?"

"No comment."

"I'll take that as a yes. Was Simpson addicted to the opioids you prescribed?"

"No comment."

"Do you prescribe opioids for a lot of your patients here, particularly service men suffering from PTSD?"

"A lot of my patients are in pain, suffering with mental anguish. I prescribe what in my professional judgement they need."

"And you saw no indication of suicide in Mr. Simpson?"

The Doctor's face turned stern. "No. But I only get to spend twenty minutes a visit, twice a month. I wouldn't necessarily spot a suicide risk. On reflection though, I guess I'm not at all surprised. What a waste."

"Suppose I told you it was murder?"

"What?"

"Suppose I told you Jeffrey Simpson didn't commit suicide at all. That he was murdered?"

"I don't understand. The papers said Jeffrey committed suicide."

"The papers were wrong."

"Murder? Who would want to kill Jeffrey?"

"I understand Simpson came into a lot of money just before he was murdered.

"Oh. I see. It was a robbery or something."

"Perhaps, perhaps not."

"Did he mention any old army friends in your conversations, Doctor?"

"No comment."

"I interpret that as a yes. Was one of his army buddies a Sam Reynolds?"

"Sam Reynolds…. It's a familiar name. Yes, they might have known each other. But that's all I can say."

Was Reynolds, or any of Simpson's other old army buddies in therapy here?"

"You're starting to be obnoxious, Judge. I can't comment."

"Do you know anyone who might want Mr. Simpson dead?"

"No. For God's sake no."

"Did you ever see Jeffrey outside of your practice here? Perhaps on the beach along The Strand, or somewhere out in public?"

"I don't fraternize with my patients."

"That wasn't my question. Did you ever see Simpson outside this facility?"

"No. And we're done here. Time's up. Good day, sir."

211

Stevens stood up from behind the protection of his desk, pointing toward the door, reaching for his phone to call his assistant just in case the Judge might resist.

"Okay, okay, Doctor, I'm leaving."

The Judge caught the glint of fear in the good doctor's eyes at his last questions about seeing Simpson outside the VA Hospital. Then he'd masked his face, not quite covering the rising pink around his cheekbones. Dr. Stevens knew more than he was saying.

CHAPTER 32

Eleven sites in three counties were raided at seven a.m. this morning in a coordinated gathering of evidence in The Strand Pre-School investigation. The police seized records, photos, videotapes, publications and weapons, but were mum about what else they found and the locations of the raids.

The TV droned on while the Judge showered and shaved. The public barrage against his clients didn't stop. He'd just have to deal with it in court. They had the jury now and the trial was starting this morning.

Two hours later the Judge entered the Superior Court room with mixed feelings. It wasn't so long ago he was on the other side of the bench, up on the dais in black robes; taring down with sharp eyes like some king in his Valhalla hall at the hoi polloi that milled about below. Dispensing justice in Los Angeles County was all high theater, lending credence and pomp to something as old as time, one member of the community judging another.

Laura Wilson turned in her seat as the Judge approached the defense table, looking pale and drawn, mouthing silently, "Thank you." She wore very faint lipstick and just the bare hint of blush on high cheekbones. She was dressed in a modest white dress with a high collar wrapping around her neck, no décolleté display today. Her flaming red hair was wrapped up in an old maid's bun at the back of her head. The only discord was a pair of high stiletto heels, matching white, encompassing nervous feet under the defense table.

Laura rose to greet the Judge and he gave her a warm hug, assuring her it would be okay, then shook Harry's hand. He pounded Barney on the back and whispered, "Okay, Barney, let's make some magic here."

Soon the room filled, mostly with press, notebooks and artist sketch pads at hand. The Clerk showed up, busied herself with a few files, then, upon a flash from the secret button at her desk, she asked all present to rise. Judge Ferguson strolled in on cue and took his position on the raised dais, his dark eyes under bushy eyebrows examining the room suspiciously, looking for who would be the first to disrupt his decorum.

Legal counsel approached the bench to discuss various procedural issues, the order of evidence, and other odds and ends before the trial could proceed. A fire-fight erupted immediately. The Judge made a motion for a closed courtroom without the press, and a gag order on both sides prohibiting release of information to the press until the jury delivered its verdicts.

"Your honor, the press has sensationalized this case out of all proportion to the demonstrable facts. The entire community has seen and heard allegations of things for which there is no shred of substantiation. The District Attorney's office has held press conferences and deliberately trotted out their interpretations of alleged events and facts they know are impossible for them to prove up in a court.. The entire public atmosphere has been poisoned, the defendants' reputations ruined, and there's no way to insulate the jury from continuing exposure to this toxic environment that is prejudicial to my clients. The best we can do now is to shut down this outside circus, close the trial to the press, and forbid the District Attorney from holding further grandstanding press conferences and releasing misleading tidbits of information to the press."

Jay Armstrong, the lead prosecutor, protested vigorously. He knew the last thing his boss wanted was a closed trial.

Armstrong argued that the public had the right to know what was going on behind closed doors. Lawyers for the Times Newspaper and the radio and TV media, present in the back because of a rumor of such a motion, were almost apoplectic, scrambling from their seats and asking to appear and be heard on the motion, squawking like disturbed crows about the constitutional right to freedom of the press and freedom of speech.

Judge Ferguson finally ruled there would be no closed trial, there would be no gag order, the press could be in the courtroom, but the press weren't to release the names or the personal information of any of children who might testify.

After all, mused the Judge cynically, Ferguson was running for re-election as well. Due process and protection of the individual's rights under the

Constitution were important of course, but first things first. One had to protect one's job.

Ferguson's ruling on the children led into another fight about how the children's testimony would be given. Armstrong wanted the kids to give their testimony in a separate room nearby with a video feed piped into the courtroom. He argued it would be damaging for the children to sit in open court and face the accused, of whom they were terrified. It would be traumatic for the children to be cross examined in front of the defendants.

Barney and the Judge counter-argued that the defendants had the constitutional right to confront their accusers which was inviolate and couldn't be taken away. Their clients had a constitutional right to face their accusers in open court, even if the accusers were children.

Judge Ferguson looked like he was waffling back and forth with each blast of heated argument, but finally sided with the defense, determining that the children would have to take the chair in the witness box in open court, just like everybody else. Jay Armstrong stomped back to his chair at the prosecution table in disgust, looking for all the world like a soccer player hamming it up after a personal foul.

Ferguson pounded his gavel ceremoniously and ordered in the jury. They marched in from a side door on the left and took their places in the jury box, eight women and four men, looking sleepy and unsure of what they were to do. Laura Wilson's fate was in the hands of these twelve people.

After further matters were dispensed with, the Judge pounded his gavel again and ordered the prosecution to present their opening statement.

Jay Armstrong stood from his table, walked to the rail of the jury box, and directed his gaze at the jury. He looked like some Baptist Minister of old addressing his flock.

"The prosecution will show the defendants, Harry Wilson and Laura Wilson, are guilty of sexually abusing fourteen children. These children were penetrated with fingers, forced to participate in copulation, coerced into playing naked games, threatened with death and bodily harm, and transported to other locations for the purpose of rousing, appealing to, and gratifying the sexual desires of Harry Wilson and Laura Wilson.

These children will testify. You will hear the same story over and over from these innocent victims. They didn't make these stories up. Again and again the children have reported the same traumatic events about the awful things were done to them. These children are all saying the same thing, because... ladies and gentlemen, because... these horrors actually happened to them.

These traumatic events are repulsive and embarrassing, but they occurred. The prosecution will also provide both medical evidence of the molestation and testimony from the parents who noticed physical and behavioral changes in their children as a result, all while they attended The Strand Pre-School.

217

This is a case about teachers who occupied a special position of trust and who exploited their position to engage in child abuse of small defenseless children.

I trust each and every one of you will do his duty and put these animals away for a long time."

He spun on one heel and marched back to the prosecution's trial table, his posture slightly stooped, like the soulful minister always destined to be a little disappointed by his flock.

The Judge then rose for the defense, inserting thumbs inside fancy red suspenders displayed inside his open sport jacket, which he hoped gave him a certain Clarence Darrow image. But he worried they just made him look fat. He strutted to the jury box and began to slowly pace back and forth in front of the jury as he spoke, looking each member in the eye in turn.

"The task for you, ladies and gentlemen of the jury, is to decide who the bad guys are here, or if they even exist.

But let me say it at the outset. Laura Wilson is not a villain. Nor is her brother, Harry Wilson. Laura and Harry are victims here, as much as the children are victims, as much as the parents are victims.

Laura and Harry Wilson have operated The Strand for more than four years, and the school itself has operated for more than thirty years. It's always been a loving and nurturing place where young children have been protected and shared wonderful memories. Laura Wilson is a modest person with a warm heart. She loves small children. She'd never do anything to hurt them. She did not molest children or kill small animals, and she didn't deceive parents. Nor did her brother, Harry Wilson.

The press, in newspapers, on television and radio, and over the internet, has published and reported licentious and outrageous stories about the defendants, filled with fictitious innuendo. Much of this reporting has been of rumors, not facts, bearing not a shred of truth to support it.. I ask you to let this vast propaganda campaign against my clients go, strike it from you minds, and open your eyes and listen and consider only the facts presented in this legal proceeding. Starting with a blank slate, to be filled only with the actual facts as proven beyond a reasonable doubt here. Indeed, that is what the law requires you to do, and what you must do.

And with that perspective in mind, right at the outset of this proceeding I want you to consider this: The State has employed three D.A.s full time in this case, five D.A. investigators, and as many as fourteen investigators at times. Twenty-two Sheriff's Task Force investigators have investigated six hundred and ninety-five families about The Strand Pre-School and its teaching staff, as well as four other pre-schools, along with the help of one full-time Ocean Hill Police detective, two full-time FBI agents and seven part-time FBI agents.

The State has searched twenty-one residences, seven businesses, thirty-seven cars, three motorcycles and one farm, looking for child pornography, nude pictures, records, diaries, evidence of mutilated animals and bank account records.

Their investigation has been carried out at a cost to the state of more than one million dollars.

And what did they find?"

The Judge paused here, heightening the tension, his hands on his hips now, staring down the jury.

"And what did they find?...

Nada... Nothing... No evidence whatsoever....

Despite these outlandish charges leaked to the media, these licentious details of things which never occurred, there is no photographic evidence, no pictures, no elicit movies of naked children, no traces of blood or semen found in The Strand Pre-School, no hidden passageways, no buried animals, no hidden tunnels beneath the school. Absolutely no corroborating evidence of any sexual abuse or molestation.

Why?...

Let me ask the question again...Why?...

Why is there no corroborating physical evidence?

Because none of it ever happened. None of it ever happened!"

The Judge lowered his voice to a whisper now, forcing some jurors to lean forward to hear.

"Because none of it ever happened, ladies and gentlemen of the jury.

We believe the State's money was well spent. Everything they investigated... and they found nothing, is evidence for the defense. They found nothing because there was nothing to find... Nothing to find, ladies and gentlemen of the jury... Nothing to find!

The children's stories, and that's all they are, were shaped and coached from them by over-zealous counselors and pressuring parents, caught up in a community hysteria that never had a basis in fact. What the children now say they remember is a contaminated mixture of fact and fantasy so absurd as to be unbelievable.

While the parents were filling out a nine-page questionnaire at the therapist offices of George Gibson, he was interviewing each child in a separate room for an hour. A review of the videotapes of these interviews will show that each child's testimony was fabricated, constructed out of whole cloth, and refined in those interviews. How you ask?...

By George Gibson's suggestions, leading questions, concerted pressure and coaching, which creates stories of molestation that never occurred.

This trial may be likened to the trials in the McCarthy Era searching for 'Pinkos', or the witch hunts of earlier times. It's the result of community mass hysteria, fanned by a yellow press concerned only with increasing circulation and audience by publishing, and even fabricating for its audience, the most outrageous stories of fiction and audacious scandal.

In the end you can reach but only one conclusion, ladies and gentlemen: Laura Wilson and Harry Wilson are innocent of any wrongdoing."

The Judge marched back to his seat and collapsed into it with dramatic flair, apparently exhausted by his dramatic and emotive speech.

At the conclusion of the day's proceedings, the Judge left the courthouse, tired, stumbling down the outside steps into a throng of newsmen, weaving his way through, muttering, "No comment."

Suddenly, Bradford Jones, the intrepid Daily Mirror reporter, emerged out of nowhere from the mass and jumble of reporters, photographers and cameramen like an evil troll, shoving a mic under the Judge's nose and shouting, "How could you possible try to close this trial to the press, Judge. Don't you believe in the freedom of the press?"

It was the final straw. The Judge whirled on him to reply.

"Not when freedom of the press is at the expense of destroying the individual's right to due process. Denying them a fair trial before an unbiased jury of their peers. Denying them the right to cross examine their accusers. Denying them the right to contest the evidence and put on their own evidence in rebuttal."

"You're so out of date, Judge. If it weren't for our investigative journalism your people would get away with everything. There'd be no trial, because no one would find out about the awful things your people secretly do."

The Judge pushed the mic away from his face and moved on, ignoring Jones's demands for a further statement.

CHAPTER 33

To sleep in the next morning, Saturday, the Judge deliberately left the TV alarm off, blissfully sleeping until his cell on the dresser rang late in the morning. At least late for him, almost nine o'clock. He got himself out of bed and groggily reached for the cell, hoping it might be a new client. It wasn't. It was one of his steady corporate accounts. Drafting contracts, minutes and such, steady $1500 a month, bread-and-butter work that sustained him between big paying matters like arbitrations and mergers. A client you could count on.

"How are you, Tim? How's your new employee working out? I got back an executed copy of his employment contract."

"That's just the thing, Judge. I want to be brief and not drag this out. We've decided to retain a new lawyer to be our corporate and contract counsel. Effective as of the end of the month. Howard James will be calling you to arrange a turnover of our files."

There was an awful pause while the truth sunk in. He was being dumped. It was like being hit with a ton of bricks.

"You weren't happy with the work Tim? Or it wasn't timely? Or if it was our fees, perhaps we could adjust them a little."

"No, no, nothing like that Judge. It's just we've been taking too much flak from customers and even our Board about your involvement in defending these filthy child-bangers; these Wilsons. Everyone feels it's time for a change."

"Oh."

"Please cooperate with Howard, he's a nice young lawyer. Fill him in, get him our files, and send us a closing bill, Judge."

There was a click. Tim had hung up.

The Judge sat back on the edge of the bed, in shock. Tim's company had been a long and steady client. This was a disaster. Was Katy was right? Was he taking his law practice into a death spiral by helping Laura Wilson? What other client would call up and fire him next? What potential business he'd been courting would quietly be shifted to some other lawyer? *Shit, Shit, Shit!*

The Judge was still muttering to himself over breakfast, but finally let it go, focusing his attention instead on a more immediate problem. Barney said the D.A. was moving closer to charging Laura Wilson with the murder of Jeffrey Simpson.

Her fingerprints were all over the maintenance room. No surprise there. Likely here DNA too, the Judge thought to himself.

She had no alibi. And the police were speculating the motive was Jeffrey's planned visit the next day to the Ocean Hill Police Department to supposedly spill his guts on her child molestation ring.

Nether Laura nor Harry needed a murder charge in the middle of this fire fight of a trial. He had to get moving on the Simpson murder case; put it to bed. He'd tracked down the surfer friend of Jeffrey's, Hank... Tanaka. He was next on the list to talk to, and the Judge knew where he usually spent his Saturday mornings: at the beach.

It was still early when he arrived on The Strand Bike Path. The morning mist along the Ocean Hill surf hadn't lifted, leaving the rollers shrouded in pastels of green and blue, their white foaming tops blending with the sky. Every so often there was a loud crack as a big wave battered the shore. The wide sandy beach was almost empty. The Judge walked toward the Lifeguard tower, faded blue, resting on its stilts at the crest of the beach. His shoes crunched in the virgin sand. The faint smell of salt and seaweed wafted about him in the soft air. It was ten a.m.

Tanaka was often here at this time if the surf was up, or do the Judge had been told. And indeed, a young Asian was bending over his leaning surfboard on the far side of the tower, industriously waxing it down. He turned as the Judge approached, mid-twenties, about five foot eight, muscular, with short black hair, bronze skin, and large friendly eyes that looked directly at the Judge, open, curious. He wore a black wetsuit, half pulled down.

The Judge hailed him. "Hi. You Hank Tanaka?"
Tanaka nodded.
"They call me the Judge. Cause I was one once." The Judge gave his best warm smile. "I'm trying to find out why Jeffrey Simpson died."
"You a detective or something now?"
"Defense counsel for Laura Wilson. Hoping you'd give me a little background on Simpson, what sort of guy he was, anything you can tell me."

Tanaka nodded his head, put down the wax, and sat down facing the sea on the wooden runway leading to the closed tower. The Judge took a seat beside him, ignoring the moisture from the dewy ramp soaking into his jeans.

"I understand you and Jeffrey were surfing buddies."

"We were for a while, but we had a falling out."

"How so?"

"It's not polite to speak ill of the dead."

"The dead don't care. They're dead. And I won't tell anyone we spoke. I'm trying to get to the bottom of what happened."

Tanaka shrugged.

"Jeff was kind of a sponge. Always borrowing money. Which never got paid back. Always angling to never pay a drinking tab. That sort of thing. I didn't mind at first. He could be a pretty funny guy, and he loved surfing. See, I grew up under the Palos Verdes Bubble, get a trust check every month; I don't mind sharing my good fortune here and there. But Jeff became kind of a pest. I got tired of having to subsidize him."

"So, you ended the relationship?"

"Not for that, actually. It was something else."

"What?"

"I'm not sure I should get into it."

"As I explained, I'm just trying to find out who Jeff really was, and what happened. Anything you tell me is confidential."

"Well… one day Jeffrey shows up with a whole lot of cash in his wallet. Maybe three grand or so. Didn't need me to buy drinks that day. And he was throwing his money around big time. Bought a motorcycle, bought everyone drinks. Got a fancy surfboard, a Chilli Rare Bird. New rubber to wear with it. For several weeks he seemed to have an inexhaustible supply of cash.

And that was okay too. I respect guys who pay back when they make a hit. Looked like he'd hit a gusher."

"You know where the cash was coming from?'

"That's the thing. He got plastered one night and told me. Tanaka took a deep breath. "The asshole was selling drugs out the back of that pre-school he worked at."

The Judge was stunned. The silence grew between them as he considered the implications.

"And that's why you ended the friendship?"

"Damn right. I don't approve of drugs. And I certainly don't approve of pushers selling them to kids and stuff. And then to be selling out of a pre-school with little kids running around. The whole idea made me sick."

"Did you tell Jeffrey what you thought?"

"I did. We had a big fight. Told him he sucked. We were both pretty drunk. He told me to fuck off, said the country owed him, got up from our table and stumbled off. We didn't talk again after that."

"When was this?"

"About four weeks ago. Saw him on a break out on the water two weeks later. I just paddled away. We didn't talk."

"Did he look cautious or worried that last time you saw him?"

"There was something disquieting about him, like maybe he was hiding on that surfboard, fifty yards off shore. I didn't wait around to talk. I just left. Wanted nothing to do with him."

"You think someone was after him?"

"Hell, I don't know."

"But you think all his newfound money came from drugs?"

"That's what he said. He was a little weasely about it, like what he was telling me wasn't all of it. Maybe he was chipping stuff on the side or something."

"You know where Jeffrey got the drugs? Who his supplier was?"

"Not directly. But I heard there's a guy, hangs out a lot at the corner of Highland and 40th, was looking for Jeffrey big time about a week before he died."

"In North Ocean Hill?"

"Yeah."

"Thanks, Hank. You've been very helpful."

"No prob' man. You surf?"

"Grew up here on the beach. But I never learned. Just body surf."

"It's a lot different, more fun than body surfing once you learn how to get up. I could teach you, Judge. I give lessons to old men."

The Judge bit his tongue, held his hand out to give a less than sincere shake, stood, turned, and crunched his way back across the sand, smoldering, muttering to himself, "*Someday Tanaka, you'll be older too. We'll see how you like being called an old man.*"

CHAPTER 34

North Ocean Hill, just before Dockweiler State Beach, was once mostly occupied by flight crews from LAX. But it had become a tony place with million-dollar shanties perched on steep slopes sliding down to the beach. All but senior pilots from the airlines had been priced out long ago.

Highland and 40th had its corners embroidered with a large gym on one side and a triplex on the other. The Judge sat in his car for about forty-five minutes, fifty feet back from the intersection on Highland, just above the gym. He watched buff young ladies trolling by, in and out of the gym in tight shorts and spandex. There were less active older specimens too in lumpy workout clothes, hiding what had slipped, fallen and expanded long ago. He listened to low volume Garth Brooks on his radio, plowing through two albums on his microchip insert.

It was a calm afternoon, about three o'clock, traffic just building along Highland, the secret route south out of the West Side at rush hour along Dockweiler Beach and into the South Bay.

About three-forty-five, a young man... well... thirtyish... everyone looked young after you passed fifty, walked past the Judge's car and took up a position on the corner of Highland and 40th, lounging against the side wall of the gym, watching traffic. He seemed relaxed; stonewashed jeans, yellow polo shirt, with a khaki vest that had seen a lot of wear, expensive-looking moccasins. He had narrow brown eyes set a little too close in an oblong head, and shaggy brown hair, clipped short across the forehead. The left-hand side of his vest pocket bulged a little.

There was some dissonance though. The bottom of a skull tattoo peeked from beneath one short sleeve of the polo. And his bland smile was betrayed by the small eyes, fugitively darting here and there about the intersection, on a 180-degree swivel as he snugged his back to the wall. When he relaxed his smile sneer lines showed, etched into a face chiseled by the elements. There was stress there too, and the hint of internal demons, making him look older, somehow hollowed out, and mean.

As the Judge watched, a teenage girl, perhaps seventeen, walked up to him, shook his hand, and muttered some greeting. His hand casually slipped into the left-hand pocket of the vest, then came out again for another handshake. The teenager wandered off down toward the beach, apparently satisfied with her transaction. The man's hand slid nonchalantly into his right-hand pocket, likely putting away cash. Five minutes later a bald man in a Cadillac convertible, newer, silver, pulled up and the man leaned over to ask directions from Narrow Eyes. This time there was only one fumbling handshake as merchandise was traded for cash, the hand going into the jacket pocket first. A regular, mused the Judge.

This continued for a forty-five minutes, six customers in various sizes, shapes and ages, sauntering up to say hello and shake hands. The pocket on the left didn't bulge so much, offset by a new bulge in the right-hand pocket… the cash pocket.

The Judge got out of his car and slowly trudged toward the corner, feeling the narrow brown eyes on him, scanning, measuring, calculating risks… cop or customer?

"Hi. Thought I might score a hit," said the Judge.

"What?" asked Narrow Eyes.

"You know, a score. I need some opioids."

"You think I look like a drug dealer, man?"

"No, no, but I was told maybe you could help."

"Who told you that?"

"Jeff Simpson."

His face tightened visibly at Simpson's name. He carefully scanned the intersection. Then he looked at the Judge in his loose-fitting Tommy Bahama shirt hanging out over his disreputable jeans, covering his pot belly. The Judge immediately lifted the bottom of his shirt up, displaying his pink tummy running up to his moth-eaten chest covered with motley tuffs of graying fur. No wire. The Judge didn't smell like a cop, and he knew it.

"Yeah, okay. Put your shirt down, man. You're calling attention."

"Okay."

"I might be able to help a little. I've got two eight-balls right now I can let you have. Thirty bucks a gram, that's one-twenty a ball, or two-forty for both."

"Got any opioids?"

"I have an endless supply, but not on me. How many you need? What kind?"

"Jeff Simpson said you'd give me a discount."

231

"Simpson's a piece of shit."

Narrow Eyes flashed anger.

"So, you haven't seen Jeff lately?"

"You kidding? The goofball's dead. Committed suicide, or so they say. Kaboom. No more Jeff. That's what happens to thieves. Mr. High and Mighties who swan around, claiming special connections… and then steal."

Narrow Eyes was almost salivating as he related this news. The Judge wondered if Narrow Eyes, or perhaps his boss, had caught up with Jeff Simpson and helped send him off to his rewards.

"So 'nough of this chit-chat. Where's your money?"

"I've changed my mind. I think I'll pass for today."

His face changed, the bland smile vanished. The brown eyes, which seemed to lack pupils now, focused on the Judge with a savage look, his features contorted into a snarl.

"You son of a bitch. You a cop? Whaddya think you're doing? playing me? If I even get a whiff of cop on you, you're a dead mother-fucker. Right here, right now!"

The Judge backed away, holding his arms out, palms outstretched in a classic stop posture.

"Yeah, you get out of here mother-fucker. And quick too," Narrow Eyes urged. "But I know you now, Homes. You're maybe going to get a visit from me. You're going to be sorry you messed with old Jack here. Yes sir. Real sorry you messed with Jack."

His glare followed the Judge back toward his car until another customer showed up. The Judge crawled behind the wheel and settled in the seat, thoughtful. He dragged his cell phone out and dialed the Ocean Hill Police Department. The grouchy sound of Detective Hardy came into his ear. "Ocean Hill Police."

"It's the Judge, Detective."

"Oh, it's you." Hardy sounded less than thrilled.

"Why does Ocean Hill have drug dealers peddling cocaine?"

"We don't have drug peddlers in Ocean Hill."

"Well I'm looking at one right now at the corner of Highland and 40th. He's doing a land-office business."

"Shit," was all the Judge got back. Then the line went dead.

The Judge suddenly felt uneasy. He looked up to find Narrow Eyes Jack looking down at him. He'd walked up from the corner and was standing beside the Judge's car, staring in through his open passenger window, listening. Jack just looked at him, licking his lips, not saying anything, perhaps anticipating the violence he would rain down. The Judge was getting the look a snake gives a cornered mouse.

Suddenly a black-and-white screeched up 40th from the beach, coming to a stop at the corner with Highland. Narrow Eyes shifted focus immediately. He turned, pasted a bland smile on his face, and sauntered north up Highland, not looking back. Two officers quickly alighted from the car and strode down 40th. Damn, the wrong direction.

Narrow Eyes turned back to look at the Judge once, hate and menace etched across his face, then disappeared uphill on 41st.   The Judge gave a big sigh of relief, but he had the nagging feeling he hadn't heard the last of Narrow Eyed Jack.

CHAPTER 35

"It is reported that the police have arrested a thirty-five-year-old bearded man in Torrance and charged him with child molestation while employed through a baby-sitting service. This looks to be another link to the wider ring of pedophiles who've terrorized the children at The Strand Pre-School, as an inside source is telling us some of the Strand kids have identified this man with the beard as one of the strangers who came and took pictures and abused them at The Strand.... This just in. The D.A. has confirmed a link between the bearded man arrested in Torrance and The Strand Pre-School molestation case."

The Judge slammed the TV off and headed for the bathroom, muttering about irresponsible reporting. The trial began in earnest this morning; there was little he could do about how the press chose to report it.

Later in the morning the two defense attorneys and the two defendants sat motionless as the prosecution called the first witness, a parent, to the stand. Armstrong justified the hearsay nature of the testimony of the parents by arguing that the primary purpose of their parental testimony was to establish the changes in behavior of their children during the time of the alleged molestation at The Strand. Over objections by Barney, the prosecution was allowed to proceed.

Doug Jones was called to the stand first. He testified that he had a daughter who attended The Strand. He had received a copy of the letter from the

Ocean Hill Police Department announcing the investigation and questioned his daughter. He then took her to Dr. George Gibson at Minor's Refuge for Change for counseling, as directed by the letter.

On cross, the Judge asked, "When you first questioned your daughter, right after you read the police letter, did your daughter say she'd been molested?"

"No, but…"

"No further questions," interrupted the Judge.

"Do you now believe you daughter was molested?" asked Armstrong on redirect.

"Yes, I do."

"And why is that?"

"Because of what my daughter told Dr. Gibson at the clinic. And because of what Dr. Gibson told me."

"Objection," snapped the Judge. "Hearsay."

"Did you file a police report on behalf of your daughter?"

"Yes."

"And did you state in that police report your daughter had been molested."

"I did."

"Because you believed that was the case."

"Yes."

The Judge stood up again for re-cross.

"Was there a financial advantage for you in filing a police report?"

"What do you mean?"

"You heard me. Was there the possibility of payment of money to you if you filed the police report?"

"Well… Dr. Gibson said my daughter needed therapy. And he's pretty expensive. I didn't have the money to pay for it. Dr. Gibson told me if I filed a police report, I might be able to get reimbursement from the Victim's Compensation Fund for my daughter's counseling."

"So, you filed the police report to get compensation for the counseling. Compensation that would be paid to Gibson, furthering the business interests of Gibson."

"Yes… No… I mean, sure, there was that, but my daughter had been molested for Christ sakes."

"Are you aware that in the taped interview with Gibson your daughter was asked if she'd ever been touched in a private place or her private parts at The Strand Pre-School, and she responded she had not been touched?"

"No."

"No more questions," the Judge said, snapping his red suspenders as he strode back to his seat at the defense table.

The next witness was Elinore Sharpton, a mother of two children whose allegations accounted for thirty-seven of the formally charged counts of molestation. She testified her two children attended The Strand Pre-School between the ages of two and five. She received the letter from the police department and questioned her children. They initially said they hadn't been touched in their private places by anyone at the school.

Because other mothers told her their kids had been molested, Elinore questioned her kids again a week later. That's when her daughter told her she saw Harry Wilson put his hands down the front of another girl's pants.

She brought her kids to Dr. Gibson for an interview. As a result of the initial interview with each child, and then consultation with Dr. Gibson, Elinore stated she was convinced both her kids had been molested.

"Were there particular policies in place at The Strand Pre-School which upon reflection you found suspicious after your consultation with Dr Gibson?" asked Armstrong.

"Yes. The Strand had a very firm policy to not allow anyone to come onto the school grounds to pick up their children during naptime."

"So, the school was essentially in 'Lockdown' during nap time?"

"Yes."

"And what do you deduce from this?"

"I believe that was the time there was rampant molestation of my children and others. The Strand rule was created as a cover for their molestation."

The Judge leaped to his feet, "Objection, pure speculation on the part of the witness without a shred of evidence to support it."

"Overruled," intoned Ferguson.

"Did you notice any differences in your children after they started attending The Strand Pre-School?" asked Armstrong.

"Yes, my kids began to have nightmares. My daughter started dancing around without her clothes off. And my son began to masturbate a lot."

On cross, the Judge pried out of Elinore Sharpton she had been concerned when she first put her children in The Strand Pre-School just because the school had a male teacher, Harry Wilson.

"Mrs. Sharpton, have you joined any parent groups formed to pursue evidence of alleged molestation of your children and others at The Strand Pre-School?" asked the Judge.

"Yes. There is a group of us that has formed a committee."

"How many are in your group, or committee?"

"Perhaps thirty parents initially, but now it's gone nationwide."

"And what's the name of your group?"

"Me Too Parents."

"And what has the committee done?'

"We've initiated an organized search to collect evidence of molestation at The Strand in order to help the police and their case."

"And what specific activities has your committee engaged in to this end?"

"We've dug up the vacant lot adjacent to the School, particularly around the apple tree on that property, looking for evidence."

"Looking for tunnels?"

"Yes."

"Looking for the graves of small animals?"

"Yes."

"Looking for evidence of rituals or rites held there on the lot, and particularly around the apple tree?"

"Yes."

"And has your group found any evidence of tunnels, shallow graves of small animals, or the occurrence of rites or rituals?"

"No." Elinore Sharpton spoke softly now.

"I can't hear you Mrs. Sharpton."

"No." In a louder voice.

"No evidence at all, right? Nothing? Nada?"

"Objection, the witness has answered the question, counsel is badgering the witness."

"Sustained.".

"No more questions," snapped the Judge.

Mary Winslow was next called to the stand by the prosecution. She testified her daughter attended The Strand and she believed her daughter had been molested there.

"How long did your daughter attend The Strand Pre-School?" asked Armstrong.

"She started on her fourth birthday and I just pulled her out when this all started, so for about a year."

"Why do you believe your daughter was molested?"

"Because when I got the letter from the police, I took her right over to Dr. Gibson for the interview.

He told me. He was very definite. He elicited the whole sordid thing from my daughter in that first interview."

Winslow gave a small little noise, like a creature in pain, which she quickly stifled.

"Did you notice any changes in your daughter after she started attending The Strand Pre-School?"

"Yes."

"What did you notice?"

"My daughter began having nightmares. I caught her masturbating in the bathroom seven or eight times. One afternoon I walked into her bedroom and she was there, lying on her younger sister, in a 69 position, fondling her sister's private parts. And her private parts were often red and swollen."

"And you attribute this conduct to the consequences of her molestation at The Strand Pre-School?"

"Yes. I believe the molestation Tammy suffered has erotized her. She's not acting normal for her age. I'm so upset."

On cross, the Judge asked. "Did your daughter, Tammy, ever say she'd been touched in a private part or bad place before she went to Gibson for counseling?"

"No."

"And you'd asked her?"

"Yes."

"And Tammy said no."

"Tammy didn't know what I was talking about."

"Did Tammy give any indication that something inappropriate had occurred at The Strand Pre-School, before she visited Gibson?"

241

"No."

"So, it was only after visiting Gibson and participating in his so-called interview session for an hour that you and Tammy decided she'd been molested?"

"Objection."

"Sustained."

"Did you have any reason to believe Tammy had been molested before she first visited Gibson?"

"Yes. From the police letter."

"And before the police letter? Did you have any reason to believe Tammy had been molested before you first read the police letter?"

"No."

"Is it true that your daughter was born with a yeast infection which has been a continuing condition for the little one since birth?"

"Yes."

"So why would you believe that red and swollen private parts were a symptom of the molestation of your daughter and not due to the continuing yeast infection?"

"Well prominent people have reinforced my belief that my child was sexually molested by the defendants at The Strand. I believe her resulting conduct and condition are a direct consequence of such molestation."

"How old is Tammy?"

"Now? Five."

"And how old was Tammy when you observed her with her sister in what you called a 69 position?"

"Almost four."

"But you've testified Tammy started attending The Strand Pre-School on her fourth birthday."

"Yes."

"So, Tammy's conduct with her sister occurred before she started attending The Strand Pre-School."

"Oh... Yes... I guess that must be right."

"No further questions."

Armstrong's next witness, Helen Rains, turned out to be both a parent and a therapist who'd actually consulted with some of the children, although not her own. She testified she immediately took her son, Jack, age five, for an interview session with Dr. Gibson after reading the police letter. Gibson told her Jack had been molested.

Barney's objection as hearsay was denied on the basis that her testimony provided a foundation for her observations of the changes in her son's behavior after attending The Strand.

"Did you notice unusual or different conduct on the part of Jack after he began attending The Strand Pre-School?" asked Armstrong.

"Yes, definitely. Jack became moody, almost melancholy at times. He became more nervous, more easily agitated. Sometimes he became angry at me. He would turn, pull his penis out, and point it at me. Jack started drawing pictures of men with very large penises, something he'd never done before. And he refused to wear underwear."

On cross, the Judge stood, flexing his suspenders again with his thumbs. "You are a trained therapist yourself, are you not?"

"Yes."

"Why is it you didn't try to interview Jack yourself, before taking him to see Gibson?"

"I did try, but Jack was very non-communicative."

"Did you ask Jack if he'd been touched in his private parts at the school by anyone?"

"Yes."

"And what did he say?"

"He just shook his head. But he looked very worried."

"So, it's fair to say Jack gave no indication he'd been molested before his counseling session with Gibson."

"Like I said, Jack looked worried when I asked him about it."

"And as a therapist, did you personally consult with some of the other children, besides Jack?"

"Yes. Dr. Gibson asked me to assist and take some of the cases. There was such a large number of kids flooding in for counseling."

"And you were paid for this counseling?"

"Of course."

"As was Gibson."

"Yes."

"Isn't there a natural conflict of interest for you to be here testifying on the stand about your son, and at the same time making money directly from the controversy surrounding The Strand Pre-School?"

"Objection."

"I withdraw the question."

The next witness, Shirley Woolen, the mother of a four-year-old son who attended The Strand, testified she visited Harry Wilson's class one afternoon, after the lunch nap and observed it was in complete chaos, with children climbing on Wilson, sitting on him, and jumping around. There was, she testified, a total lack of discipline.

"Was there any change in your son's conduct after he began attending The Strand Pre-School?" asked Armstrong.

"Yes. George started refusing to take his underwear off at night, despite my protests. He began spending long periods, like an hour or more, in the bathtub, doing who knows what. Several times he danced around in his underwear in front of me and his dad. He quite suddenly became very afraid of the dark. And one time I heard George singing the naked movie star chant."

Again, on cross, the Judge extracted the admission the mother had not thought her son might have been molested until after the police letter, and hadn't become convinced something had happened until after the interview session with Gibson.

The parade of witnesses continued all day. One parent testified that her son complained that his 'fanny hurt'. Another testified she'd picked up her three-year-old and couldn't wake him up. "He was real sleepy, like maybe he'd been drugged," she said. Another said her child was frightened because he continued to see "those bad people" driving around the neighborhood. Several parents testified their children were afraid of needles and shots. One parent broke down in tears, testifying her child had been diagnosed with herpes of the mouth.

Some parents expressed anger and other strong emotions against the defendants during their testimony. One mother requested Barney to, "Stand away from those defendants, those Wilsons, when you ask your questions. I don't want to look at either of them." Pointing a finger at the defendants.

As Armstrong elicited damning testimony from each parent, the Judge and Barney took turns jumping up to object, arguing the parent's testimony produced no creditable information to support the criminal allegations against the defendants in the case; the testimony lacked forensic verification of what was alleged to have occurred, such as pictures or film; the testimony constituted hearsay, since it was a secondhand account of what the child said they experienced; and the testimony didn't substantiate that child molestation actually took place.

Ferguson consistently denied their objections, ruling the parents' testimony was foundation and support for the children's testimony to come, and also relevant as to the behavioral changes in the children because of their attendance at The Strand Pre-School.

It was a long and brutal day. The Judge felt wrung out like a wet blanket as he stumbled from the courtroom amongst the mass of reporters stampeding for the hallway and air space to use their cells and file their reports.

Later, the Judge pulled up to his Palos Verdes driveway in the early evening, collected his mail at the bottom of the driveway, and slowly made his way up to his front steps. Katy didn't meet him at the door as she usually did. That should have been a tip off. But his mind was on the court case, the witness testimony, and his next move.

He used his key to let himself in, and headed toward the kitchen, where the door was blocked by Annie the Dog, sitting on her haunches, her tail flat, no welcome for him. She gave him a sour expression, then slowly got up, her tail going into a full circle over her back, and marched away stiff-legged legged, ignoring him. What the hell was going on?

He spotted Katy with her back to him, sitting in the breakfast room, staring out at the Santa Monica Bay, dark now, lighted only by the Queen's Necklace of lights along the Esplanade in Redondo Beach, and the ring of lights along the coast all the way to Malibu. A few firefly lights of aircraft circled into the landing pattern at LAX. Off in the distance the lighted skyscrapers of downtown protruded up from the great L.A. Plain like a collection of sparkly mushrooms in varying lengths and sizes. It was a quiet and peaceful scene.

The Judge sat down at the table beside her. She turned to look at him, her eyes moist, her mascara running, tear streaks drying down her cheeks.

"Honey, what's happened?"

She just looked at him for a moment, eyes growing cold. He reached to touch her cheek where a tear had been. But she brushed his hand away.

"I ran into a reporter today," she said coldly, "A Bradford somebody."

"Bradford Jones."

"Yes."

"A complete asshole, Katy."

"Perhaps, but he asked me for a statement, shoved a mic under my nose."

"What'd he want?"

"Wanted to know how I felt as your wife, for human interest he said, watching you defending Laura Wilson, a woman you'd had an affair with."

"Son of a bitch… that bastard."

"You should have told me." Katy's voice was raising now. "You're the son of a bitch, Judge. You should have told me. You're a complete asshole."

"I figured you wouldn't want to know."

"Bullshit, Judge."

"I'm sorry, Katy."

"Judge, he asked if I thought it was a conflict of interest for you to represent a client you'd had an affair with."

"What did you say?"

"What could I say. I don't know anything about your stupid lawyers' cannons of ethics. All I know is lawyers lie, cheat, avoid being honest, and use words and semantics to twist things so they're different from what really happened. And the smarter the lawyer, the better they are at twisting and obfuscating the truth."

"Katy."

"So I told him to fuck off."

"Good, Katy. That's just what I told him too."

"It's not good, Judge. It's awful. How can I ever trust you again?"

"Oh, Christ, Katy. Remember we agreed not to talk about past lovers. This was years ago."

"This is different Judge and you know it. You're in a relationship with this woman again."

"I'm not having an affair with her, Katy."

"You're in the second most personal relationship with her you can have. You're her defense lawyer. And you had an affair with her before and you didn't tell me. All my friends are going to see the article he publishes. I'm going to look like a damn fool. And wait till my mother reads it... and oh, and my dad."

Katy was yelling now, springing from her chair to tower over him, hands on her hips. "You're a complete prick, Judge, and you're not sleeping with me tonight, or any night soon." She turned away, starting to leave the room.

"But Katy, this is ridiculous. This what I do. I defend people. She needed defending. The distant past is just old news."

Katy turned back, a glint in her eyes now. "Old news... Old news..."

Katy suddenly swung her fist with all her might, twisting as her dad had taught her to throw all her body weight into it, landing a blow to the Judge's shoulder he felt all the way to his feet, nearly knocking him out of his chair.

Then she turned and marched out, tall, proud, holding her hand that had struck the blow cradled in the other. It looked injured.

Annie leaped up, gave the Judge a disdainful look, tail at full curl, and marched after Katy.

Christ, where was little Ralphie when he needed his son the most? Things would have been more civil if Ralphie had been here. He could have used Ralphie for protection. The Judge marched into the kitchen and poured himself three fingers of Laphroaig, not bothering with ice, massaging his shoulder with his other hand, feeling sorry for himself.

CHAPTER 36

That night and the next morning, the only thing the Judge had to keep him company was bad news. The news coverage of the trial.

As each distraught parent had left the courthouse after their testimony, coming out the front door of the ponderous building and down its steps to the street, they were met by a gaggle of news people and cameras, everyone wanting statements, explanations, descriptions of feelings, and so on. Several mics were shoved under their noses each time and provocative questions asked, most designed to elicit emotive responses.

It worked. Several parents, emotional and no longer under oath to speak only what they knew as fact, took the opportunity to portray Laura and Harry Wilson as evil incarnate, preying on the youngest and weakest in society, destroying innocent childhoods and scarring their children for life. One parent proclaimed reason the kids were now so afraid of doctors was because of painful physical examines and rectal temperatures taken during the 'Doctor Game'. Another generalized that a dozen kids had told parents that they'd been given pink pills and pink liquids which everyone was sure had been drugs. The Wilsons were called monsters who didn't deserve a trial and should be immediately locked away forever, or worse.

Representatives of the online group, Me Too Parents, gave statements on what they believed happened and how they believed the Wilsons should be punished, even though most were not parents of the alleged victims and had no first-hand knowledge. They kept using the word 'creditable', as though it was a of mantra that automatically established the truth of a matter. Creditable stories, creditable sources, creditable accounts, creditable children, creditable parents… and so it went. It was a circus, choreographed, taped, and replayed repeatedly on multiple channels across the broadcast news e and in the newspaper headlines the next day.

The next morning the Judge was desperate for a respite from the howls of a press gone mad. He kept the TV off and didn't open his newspapers. There was no court today and he'd arranged to meet Jeffrey Simpson's ex-wife.

Louisa Simpson had reverted back to her maiden name, Louisa McFarland, after their divorce. She rented a small bungalow in North Hermosa, well above Pacific Coast Highway and far from the water. The Judge had gotten her contact information from Jeffrey Simpson's brother, called, and she'd reluctantly agreed to meet the Judge before she left for her work. She was a real estate salesperson with Diamonds in the Rough Realty.

He pulled up and parked on the curve next to a modest white clapboard house, all lawn and rose beds in front, ranch style, Fifties, a vintage magnolia tree shedding white blossoms like tears across the front lawn.

Louisa opened the door on his first ring, a tall willowy woman, early thirties, still pretty, but with stress lines around the eyes and mouth, typical of real estate people who had to be tough to survive. Particularly once they'd run through their initial list of family and friends needing brokerage services.

She extended a small slender hand which delivered a surprisingly firm handshake. Then she swung around the counter dividing the living room from the kitchen and swooped down to retrieve two beers from the refrigerator, squatting in her tight olive skirt and matching short coat, displaying a scrawny rump. She had dark brown hair tied back in a ponytail and the long angular face of an athlete.

"There's not much I can tell you about Jeff, Mr.… err…"

"Judge. Just call me Judge."

"Judge. We weren't close after the divorce."

"When was the divorce?"

"Finalized a year ago."

"What happened?"

"Afghanistan happened. He went off to war one person, came back somebody else. I didn't know him anymore."

"How so?"

"Jeff initially seemed okay when he came back. He'd lost weight of course, and they'd picked a little shrapnel out of him when the truck he was driving blew up, but he was happy to be home and with me."

"That changed?"

"Yes. Within six months he started having nightmares about being in Afghanistan. He started sleeping only two or three hours at a time. The rest of the night he was up prowling around the house. He insisted on keeping a loaded gun in his nightstand, even though he knew I was afraid of guns. He was verbally abusive at times; it seemed any little thing or even just a sharp noise would set him off. He'd get angry way out of proportion to what was happening.

He said crazy things too, like he should have died with the other members of his team. It wasn't fair for God, or fate, or whatever, to single him out. I knew he was depressed. But I didn't know how to help. He no longer had any sexual interest in me. He seemed guarded whenever we talked. I couldn't break through. It was like he was perpetually numb inside.

He said something very interesting once back then. Said, 'I wanted to keep the war away from you, Louisa. But somehow, I brought the war home with me every time I stepped into our house.'"

"And that continued?"

"Actually, it got worse. He started to drink more after work. He'd come home plastered and collapse into bed. Then I found some little plastic bags of white pills in his tool box. He got quite angry over that. Accused me of spying."

"Opioids?"

"Yes. Between the drinking and the drugs, he started regressing physically. He found it difficult to focus. He couldn't make it to work on time. He had a job as a programmer back then. But his boss complained he was moving slower and slower around the office, was late coming in half the time, always leaving early. They finally fired him.

That was the final straw for me. I wasn't going to support him so he could lay around, booze, surf and do drugs. I kicked him out and filed."

"How'd he take the divorce?"

"Badly. By then Jeff couldn't keep a job. Couldn't help with the rent. Couldn't hold a decent conversation. Sucked in bed. Suddenly didn't want kids. The only thing that turned him on was 'turning on'. Booze, weed, cocaine when he could score some, whatever he could find in the medicine cabinet otherwise. He didn't give a shit about me. I was just the one with an income stream he could suck up to support his habit."

"Did he contest the divorce, the property settlement, or anything?"

"Everything. Cheap bastard. There wasn't much to fight over. But he wanted it all so he could fund his good times. We were on the edge of a trial when a settlement was finally worked out. He kept his car and his computer equipment. I got my car, our furniture, a life insurance policy, the cash in the bank, my commissions on deals ready to close, and we were done. Oh, and he got the dog. Mean little mix, hated me. In the end, Jeff loved that bastard more than he loved me. Anyway, Jeff wasn't the man I married. He was some stranger with Jeff's face. By the time the divorce was over I hated his guts."

"Were his problems related to post-traumatic stress?"

"Oh yeah. That's what they like to call it, if you believe in that crap. I think he just got into drinking and drugs and liked the way it felt, the way he could escape all responsibility."

"Did the VA help?"

She snorted. "Oh sure. He'd go down there and whine at them twice a month for twenty minutes; con opioids out of the doctor. A lot of good that did. Long lines, disinterested staff, mini-minute consultations and then the bum's rush out the door. Just so they could flow through more patients and make their statistics look better. Assholes."

"What was the insurance policy you got out of the divorce?"

"One just like his mother has. Seven hundred and fifty thousand. Guess I get that now. Jeff's better for me dead than alive." She tried to chuckle but it sound forced.

"When's the last time you saw him?"

"About a week ago. He still owed me money for the credit cards I had to pay off. I had to chase him down. Found him in his favorite bar on the Hermosa Pier that evening, Shucky's. Smashed as usual."

"Did he pay you?"

"Surprisingly enough, he did. Right on the spot. Had a whole damn lot of hundreds in his wallet. He'd scored somewhere."

"What'd you think about his job at the pre-school?"

"A joke. Jeff could stay sober for eight hours or so. Even sound quite rational and mellow. Then he'd slide away to his favorite pain-killer. That job wasn't going to last and we both knew it."

"Any history of sexual deviance, spousal abuse, confused sex roles, anything like that?"

"Jeff?" She snorted. "He liked his woman experienced and meaty. Always complained I was too skinny. I don't think he's a candidate for what was going on at that pre-school. Jeff wouldn't have been involved. Wasn't his style. In fact, I think he had no sexual interest in anything. Just a dud after Afghanistan. He was trapped, no career, no future, no way to move forward. Couldn't go back to the Army. Spending all his money on drugs and booze. Said it helped the pain. But I never thought he'd hang himself?"

"Is that what you think happened?"

"Shit, I don't know. That's what the paper said."

"It wasn't suicide, Louisa, it was murder."

Louisa gasped as her hand flew across her mouth, eyes wide, in shock.

The Judge asked, "Know where he scored his drugs?"

Louisa's face got tight, cautious now. "I don't do drugs."

"Okay, but you've said Jeff did. Do you know where he got them? I'm not the police, this stays just between us."

"There's a guy, hangs around North Ocean Hill, around Highland and 40th, Jack, or Jacky or something. Jeff said he was a dangerous dude. Jeff would buy stuff from him I think."

"What'd he buy?"

"Weed, cody, white horse, octagons, blues, shit I don't know, whatever the guy had. I think more recently Jeff was using a lot of opioids."

"Why do you think that?"

"Cause when he opened his wallet at Shucky's, a pack of them fell out."

"Opioids?"

"Yes. But it wasn't just that."

"What then?"

"Jeff offered me the opioid pack, six pills. He'd never do that; he'd keep them for himself for sure. Unless he was absolutely rolling in them."

CHAPTER 37

The Judge rose with a yawn and padded across the floor to switch the TV off, so jaded he was almost immune to the daily reports of additional grisly details about The Strand Case. The D.A. was grand-standing again. It was said her ratings in her re-election battle were up another two points since The Strand trial started.

At 9 am the Judge entered the courtroom and settled at the defense table between Barney and Laura. Laura took his hand under the table in a death-squeeze as they waited for the grand entrance of Judge Ferguson.

Once things got under way, Armstrong called Dr. George Gibson to the stand. Gibson strolled in through the rear doors of the courtroom looking as natty as ever, this time in black silk slacks, white turtleneck, and black silk sport jacket. No tie. An outfit outside the norm of customary dress for testifying experts. But a slick outfit if you were advertising yourself as a therapist available for hire through cameras waiting on the front steps of the courthouse. The Judge watched Armstrong, cringe at Gibson's outfit. Good!

Armstrong qualified Gibson as an expert and elicited that Gibson had conducted videotaped interviews of the children who were the subject of the sexual abuse.

"Tell us about your technique in interviewing the children, Dr. Gibson," asked Armstrong.

"It is a careful process. I'd liken it to putting together a jigsaw puzzle about what actually happened to each child at The Strand Pre-School. I follow Dr. Roland Summit's accepted theory on the Child Sexual Abuse Accommodation Syndrome, which states that children never lie about sexual molestation."

"And exactly how do you conduct this examination?"

"I start with open-ended questions, slowly drawing the child out, becoming more specific in my questions as the child becomes more comfortable. I encouraged each child to express themselves by using puppets and dolls which are without clothes and have accurate sex organs, to assure we are both talking about the same thing.

I tell each child that the other children have already told me what happened at the school, so as to remove any stigma that a child is somehow ratting on another child. I deliberately apply labels like 'naked' and 'yucky' to childhood games involving nudity and touching, so as to have agreed terms for what went on at the school that are easily understood and easy to communicate. I encouraged the children to demonstrate what happened at school with the puppets and pointers."

"And you stand by these methods?"
"I do."

"My distinguished defense counsel has observed the videos of your counseling sessions with several of the children and has argued that some of your techniques may tend to induce a child to construct or fabricate a memory that is not a reality. How do you respond to his criticism?"

"I don't believe I could have implanted the memories of molestation the children already have of what happened to them at The Strand Pre-School. When you interview over fifty children and you keep hearing over and over the same things from so many different kids: naked games, private place touching, adults taking pictures, secret trips off campus, the torture and killing of small animals, and so on, you get a pretty clear picture."

"So, you believe the incidents reported in the video interviews of the children actually occurred?"

"I do."

After further questioning, Armstrong turned the witness over to the defense for cross examination, causing Barney to dart from the defense table like a thoroughbred leaving the gate.

"Dr. Gibson, what is the Child Sexual Abuse Accommodation Syndrome?" Barney asked.

"The Syndrome is the theory which explains a child's reaction to sexual abuse. The syndrome is composed of five categories, of which two define basic childhood vulnerability and three are sequentially contingent on sexual assault. The first two are secrecy and helplessness. The second three are: entrapment and accommodation; delayed, unconvincing disclosure; and retraction."

"Yes, well, isn't it true that this theory has been discredited?"

"No. There is of course some controversy regarding the theory, and it has been the focus of debate in the psychological and legal fields."

"Hasn't the debate focused on whether the model can be used to accurately diagnose sexual abuse at all?"

"I suppose there has been debate about that, yes. But in my professional opinion the model works."

"Dr Gibson, since you used puppets, do you believe puppet use suggested to the children that your interview was merely a game. Suggested they were therefore free to fabricate details about what occurred at the school?"

"No, I do not."

"You stated you told the children you already knew about naked games that occurred at the school. Do you believe your statements in this regard encouraged the children to fabricate details about naked games?"

"I do not. Telling the child that I already knew about the naked games was designed to remove any burden or concern the child might have about the repercussions of telling what really went on at the school. It is a recognized counseling technique. I do not believe this technique encouraged the children to make up facts, and I saw no evidence that the facts they reported were made up."

"Do you believe, Mr. Gibson, that abuse went on for several years at The Strand Pre-School?"

"Yes, I do."

"How do you explain that such rampant abuse, if it actually occurred, was not discovered sooner?" asked Barney.

"I can't explain that."

The Judge got up next, trading places with Barney.

"Are you a Licensed Social Worker in California?"

"No."

"In fact, you aren't licensed at all as any type of therapist, psychotherapist, or other medical professional, either in California, or anywhere, are you?"

"No."

"Mr. Gibson, you are a self-proclaimed expert on the molestation and abuse of small children, are you not?"

"I have considerable experience in the field. I've interviewed children who have been the victims of molestation, I've provided counseling to help children through recovery from the emotional damage as a result of such molestation, I've written papers on the subject and given lectures on the subject, and yes, I believe I am a well-qualified expert."

"Have you, yourself, ever been the victim of molestation, whether as a child, or otherwise, Mr. Gibson?"

"I don't have to answer that." Gibson sputtered. That's privileged. It's not relevant to my testimony." Gibson's face turned red with anger.

"Objection," Armstrong belated yelled, jumping to the defense of his star witness.

"Objection sustained. Counsel, move on," ruled Ferguson.

"You videoed the children's interviews you conducted."

"Yes."

"And you showed the video interviews to the parents of each of the children."

"Yes."

"But did you only show your entire video of each interview to each parent, or only certain segments?"

"I don't know what you mean."

"Isn't it a fact that you mostly showed the parents selective segments of the taped interview where the child alleged some sort of molestation conduct. But, you did not show the parent your earlier discussion with the child leading up to that disclosure, including specifically denials by the child that anything had happened?"

"The earlier stages of the interview, when I was developing rapport with the child, were not relevant."

"Oh, I think they were quite relevant."

"Objection, counsel is testifying for the witness."

"Sustained."

On re-direct, Armstrong asked Gibson, "In your professional opinion, Doctor, were the children drugged?"

"Yes. I found that several of the children related experiences of being given pills, shots and liquid drugs that made them drowsy."

"Could that account for failure to discover this sick pedophile ring sooner?"

"Yes. That may very well be the reason."

"Objection. Pure speculation," shouted Barney. "Sustained."

Finally, the afternoon's testimony was over. Ferguson pounded his gavel with authority, declaring, "We will recess for today, and begin again tomorrow."

The Judge needed a caffeine fix to restore his flagging energy before he made the long drive back to Palos Verdes. Something sweet he decided, since Katy wasn't around to scold. Perhaps a Salted Caramel Mocha Frappuccino.

As he stepped into the line at Starbucks around the corner from the courthouse, he felt a pull at his sleeve from behind. Turning around he found himself face to face with reporter Bradford Jones. Shit, was the guy stalking him?

"Is it true Judge, that late yesterday afternoon The Strand structure was set on fire again, and a half hour ago certain lady inmates in the Los Angeles City Jail set fire to your client's red hair?"

"How is that relevant to anything, except the lack of humanity of some people in the way they treat others, Bradford?"

"Human interest, Judge, human interest."

"You mean it sells newspapers."

"We all got to make a living, Judge. At least I don't sell my time for service getting child molesters off."

The Judge turned and stomped away, his appetite for a Frappuccino suddenly gone.

CHAPTER 38

As the Judge started home he brooded about the case, and particularly the possibility the D.A. would bring on a murder charge. He ran over the things he knew and the things he suspected about Jeffrey Simpson's death as he heel-and-toed the pedals down the Harbor Freeway in the miserable L.A. traffic, heading for Palos Verdes.

He kept coming back to the maintenance room. There was something there he'd missed? What was it? On a whim he cut over at the last possible second to catch the turnoff onto the 405 Freeway North, generating a blaring calliope of horns, waving hands and middle fingers. He barely missed a large truck and gave a little Asian woman in a small Honda a heart attack, but he made it. Some days he had the feeling his driving was approaching the level of Mr. Magoo. Particularly when he was driving and thinking about a case at the same time.

He got off at Rosecrans, turned left on Inglewood, and right on Ocean Hill Boulevard, taking him down to the center of Ocean Hill, to The Strand Pre-School.

The school was closed, the children long gone, the staff dispersed to other jobs, except for his two clients who languished in jail.

A foreclosure notice was pinned to The Strand's front door and there was burnt wood and blackened stucco along a patch of the front wall of the structure, the apparent result of a recent fire hastily put out.

The Judge used the key Laura had given him to open the entrance door, stepped in, and made his way down the long hall to the left, to the maintenance room. As he approached, he heard a rustling coming from inside the room. Rats? A ghost? No one else was supposed to be here. He eased the key into the lock and tried to turn the key and swing the door open in one fluid move. But the door caught, then creaked in protest as it swung, the squawk echoing around the room.

No one was in the room. He got his cell out and used its light, walking to the other end of the room. He reached the window at the other end of the room. Its curtain had been removed, giving a dirt-filtered view of the sunset as the outside light faded. He darted around the end of the rack, prepared to come face to face with some kid, or a homeless person looking for shelter. But the narrow corridor behind was empty. It must have been a rat.

He walked down to the middle of the long space between the wall and the shelving, and out of curiosity used his cell phone light to examine the wall opposite the shelving. It was old plywood paneling, un-stained, deep orange with age, nailed no doubt to two-by-four framing behind. Here Simpson's blood had pooled and then run under the wall where it met the concrete.

As he brought the light closer, in the middle of the wall he noticed a floor-to-ceiling central panel without nail heads showing around its seams. He shined the light to the ceiling. Just faintly he could see what looked like one half of small, discreet hinges, six of them, inset into the plywood ceiling above. Perhaps the other half was attached to the other side of the wall panel.

He pressed against the panel. Nothing happened. He felt with his fingers for some lock or catch. There was none. Puzzled, he brought his light closer and carefully examined the vertical seams of the panel. He pressed there. The plywood seemed solid, firmly affixed to the framing behind it. But there were no nails.

There were knotholes here and there in the plywood, with the dark brown of the interior layer of plywood exposed. He shone his light on them. One of them seemed to have dirty smudges built up around it, smudges the other knotholes lacked. He put his finger into the smudged knothole, against its dark brown interior layer of plywood, and pressed. It gave way. Suddenly the whole panel, plywood, two-by-four framing and all, swung silently out and upward to the ceiling, propelled by springs built into the side walls of the interior framing.

The Judge shined his cell phone light in, lighting two concrete steps. He bowed his head and wiggled down the two steps, standing erect again below on a concrete floor, old and cracked, defining a space smelling of dust and mildew. A large water heater was happily humming to one side. A rusty old furnace stood forlorn and silent to the other.

At the other end of the small room were steps going back up, and above them a double trapdoor, mounted at an angle to the vertical, as they did for cellars in the old days. The Judge reached up and pushed one half of the door. It willingly flopped open, exposing the side yard of the school and the darkening sky above. The trapdoor wasn't locked.

The Judge pushed the other half of the trapdoor open and clambered out into long green grass in the narrow side yard of The Strand structure. Apparently, the turf here was not covered in the maintenance man's duty to cut the grass. There was no fence here. The rear fence of the play yard dovetailed into the rear corner of the building and did not run the length of the side line. The grass ahead of him was trampled somewhat into a faded path leading off across the vacant lot and up toward the street behind the school.

The Judge followed the faint trail though the tall grass and across the vacant lot. Although it was almost dusk now, the trail was easy to see through the tall green mustard, sprouting with yellow. It weaved under the old apple tree where the Devil reputedly lived, and then ran across the lot all the way to the curve of the street behind the school. The Judge could feel his nose drip from the grass, wet now with dew, a product of his mild hay fever. He could feel several small insects sneaking up his pantlegs, happy to take a nip of the interloper. He swatted at one leg with desperation and then the other, hoping to dislodge the feeding residents.

He reached the street and looked up and down it. There was no one to see. Two houses down and across the street, a garage door was open and a light was on. The judge walked over and peered in from the curb. A young man was there, industriously waxing down his bodyboard, a Lucky Bums Board, all fuchsia and red. He was too intent to notice the Judge. The boy looked perhaps twelve or thirteen, slender, sporting a crew-cut and a tan skin from lots of sun. The Judge walked up the driveway and paused just outside the line of the garage.

"Nice looking board. You surf too?"

The young man looked up and gave the Judge a quick smile.

"Hi. Naw, surfboards are too much of a hassle. You gotta drag the damn thing around, then sit on it for long stretches at a time just to catch a righteous wave. A bodyboard now, it gives you an instant ride. And it fits over your handle bars."

"What's your name? They call me just 'Judge', cause I was one once."

"Dan. Dan Ortega."

"Nice to know you, Dan. I'm trying to find out what's been happening over there, across the lot, at the pre-school."

"The Strand Pre-School? Good luck with that. It's closed you know. They were molesting children."

"I heard. You ever seen anything going on over there?"

"Me?" Dan looked up at the Judge. "No, not officially."

"What about unofficially?"

"They were a bunch of weirdos coming and going at all hours of the night. Devil worshippers, I heard."

"Really? Did they have marches and torches and stuff?"

"Probably. I didn't see any of that. But my bedroom's right here, next to the garage. Faces that way. Midnight, one in the morning, I'd hear, sometimes see people parking their cars or motorbikes, tromping through the vacant lot to the back of the school. Coming and going, trying to be real quiet, like some secret cult meeting or something."

"Did you talk to the police? Tell them about it?'

Dan's face turned worried. He looked behind him at the door leading to the interior of the house.

"I'm not supposed to talk about it. My mom says to keep my mouth shut and stay out of trouble. I'm not supposed to tell anyone. Forget what I said, Mister."

The door to the interior of the house suddenly flew open and a woman stepped down the one step into the garage. Dark hair, black eyes slightly slanted, matching high cheekbones, late thirties or early forties. Clearly the mother.

"What's going on?" she asked, looking directly at the Judge.

"Hi. They call me the Judge. I was…."

"I know who you are. You're the degenerate who's trying to get those pedophiles across the street off. I don't want you talking to my son. I don't want you on my property. We don't know anything, and we aren't saying anything. Now vamoose, go… before I call the police."

She pointed an outstretched finger at the Judge as though it was a secret weapon and then waved it around in a circle, pointing above his head.

The Judge put his hands up defensively, backing out of the garage, then spun around and retraced his steps, across the street and into the tall mustard of the vacant lot where the insect inhabitants welcomed his legs' return. He moved back along the faint path across the lot and under the apple tree, back down the steps into the boiler room, closing the cellar doors again, his face red with contained anger at the mother's epithet.

The Judge made his way back through the little room and up narrow steps, stepping through the paneled wall. A small wooden knob was recessed in the framing that surrounded the opening. The Judge pulled it and the plywood panel noiselessly swung down and back into place.

He walked carefully down the narrow passage alongside the shelving and around to the daybed and sat down on the silk bedcover to contemplate the room. He glanced again at the cover, all violet and flowers, Laura's cover. Shit, why hadn't she told him?

The Judge glanced at the old TV sitting opposite the daybed. Did they watch movies late at night? More fun stuff than that, likely. He leaned over and turned the TV on, just as he'd done before. The same Spanish channel came on. But Jeffrey didn't speak Spanish, at least according to his mother. And neither did Laura.

He switched the TV off and slid it halfway off the shelf, tipping it down so he could see behind it. A small patch antenna was plugged into it next to the power cord. He looked behind it on the shelf. There was an HDMI cord laying there, looking innocuous, old and dusty. On a whim he pulled the cord out and plugged it into the female jack on the back of the set. Then he slid the TV back onto its shelf and turned it on.

The Spanish channel didn't come up. Instead the screen was split into four separate color screens. *Damn!* One screen showed the Judge, staring back at himself from the day bed. God he was a handsome devil… not. He smirked at the thought and waved at himself.

The second screen showed The Strand's long corridor leading on the other side of the maintenance room's entry door. One could see if someone was coming toward the room, or lingering outside the door to listen. Listen to what? Laura was not only wild and demonstrative in bed, but she was loud. Loud all to way up to when she came. Then she was really loud.

It was a good job the maintenance door was solid. They wouldn't have wanted Laura's screams echoing down the hall of The Strand Pre-School during lunch. Even so, someone standing close to the outside of the door would likely enjoy a muffled sound show. This was perhaps an early warning to tone things down… maybe.

Screen three was a view outside of the building, on the side next to the vacant lot where he'd just been.

There was the small trapdoor, extending at an angle out from the building, and the path amongst the weeds out across the lot. The last screen showed in night mode the dimly lit boiler and furnace room he'd just been in.

The Judge stood up and examined the old dusty boxes stacked on the shelving behind the TV. Behind the first box on the left, cardboard and filled with old plumbing parts, was a wooden storage box, topped out with dusty extension cords and two old light fixtures, likely from some ancient bathroom. But when he pulled the box out a little, it resisted. He tilted the box up and looked behind it. There was a fresh round hold drilled on its back side near the bottom and a new electrical cord ran out. Interesting.

He carefully unpacked the box's contents, and removed a false bottom about two thirds of the way down to show a video recorder, nestled in silence, happily blinking its green power indicator at him. He pressed the open button, and the tray for a DVD to slide out. It was empty. Still, this was too elaborate not to have been used. Jeffrey Simpson, or someone, had videoed this daybed, no doubt with Laura in residence, and also the comings and goings of some person or persons through the trapdoor and from The Strand hall.

What had been on the videos recorded here?

CHAPTER 39

The Judge sat back on the daybed and thought some more. He looked at himself again on the TV, fancying this time he looked like 'The Thinker', lost in thought. A movement caught his eye at the trapdoors on the screen. *Son of a bitch, one of them was opening.*

The Judge got up and softly strolled around the other side of the shelving to the panel door, pushing the knot again, causing it to silently open. It was dark out now, and even darker in the furnace room. With his cell light off he could barely make out where the trapdoor was located.

Half the trapdoor was open, and now the second half was opening. A beam of light, likely from another cell, came on and displayed the steps leading down. Cautiously, a pair of shoes began the descent.

The shadow of the person came in view, moving softly across the concrete floor of the furnace room to the water heater mounted on a wooden platform, the narrow beam of his cell light leading the way. The Judge tried not to breathe, motionless in the dark, perched on the steps leading down from the maintenance room.

He heard rustling, then the muffled squeak of plywood being pried up further back in the boiler room.

He eased down another step into the boiler room. The shape was crouching over by the large water heater. The shape had the cell light protruding under one arm, while he used a small crowbar to pry up a strip of the top wood of the platform on which the heater sat. One strip came off and was leaned against the box. There was a horrific screech as a second strip of wood came loose.

The figure froze, listening. The Judge wished his heart would quiet. Thirty seconds went by.

The figure moved again, pulling the second strip of wood up and away, piling it with the first. His hands thrust greedily into the space exposed. There was a rustle like dry leaves, the cell light bobbing in all directions under his arm. His hands came out holding a large plastic bag of red and white pills. He carefully put the bag aside. Both hands disappeared again, coming up with a second and then a third plastic bag, each filled with more white pills.

As he wrapped his arms around the bags, rising, the cell light slipped from under his arm, falling with a crash to lean against the side of the platform, framing the man in light. It was Narrow Eyed Jack. Jack grabbed the light and perhaps on instinct, directed it around the room, stopping when it lit up the Judge watching from the step below the paneled doorway.

Jack and the Judge jumped at the same time, startled. Jack dropped his third sack of pills back into its resting place, made a small sound, half anguished, half angered, scooped his two retrieved sacks, and bolted up the steps and out the trapdoor like a jackrabbit.

The Judge held himself tight, not allowing himself to move, and counted, 1-2-3-4… He counted to one hundred. He didn't want a run-in with a man thirty years his junior, wielding a crowbar. Then the Judge quietly eased across the concrete floor, up the steps at the trapdoor, and out.

Jack was gone. But he'd gotten a part of what he'd wanted.

The Judge closed the trapdoors and slowly followed the heavily traveled path in the weeds, out and across the empty lot next door to the curb of the street behind The Strand. No Narrow Eyed Jack was to be seen. He stood at the curb of the street and tried to sort it out.

What did Jack know? He knew about the drug stash. He must have known drugs were being sold here at the side of the school, perhaps his drugs, his inventory. Was he a wholesaler, selling a supply to Jeffrey who apparently conducted a retail distribution in drugs? Did he know about the panel? This secret access to the maintenance room? Did he have a hand in Jeffrey's death? Narrow Eyed Jack certainly looked capable of murder.

That's when the light came on at the side of his face, blinding him. He put his hand up to shield his eyes. As he did so he saw the gun, held in a second hand below the light, pointed at his chest. It was always surprising how very large the gaping hole in space looked, when you were staring down the barrel of a gun pointed at your chest. His heart raced. He thought he might be sick.

The Judge slowly put his hands up, palms out, the classic stance of surrender. He had no choice. He could feel his face turn pale in the light as the blood drained from it, wondering what the bullet smashing into his chest would feel like?

A gravelly voice from behind the light spoke.

"Put your hands down, Judge, you look silly."

The light moved up briefly to display the holder of the gun. Thank God. It wasn't Narrow Eyed Jack. The Judge saw the smiling face of Bill O'Neal, Ocean Hill's Police Chief.

The Judge slumped, relief spreading through him, feeling weak.

"Why don't you sit down."

He looked at the raised curb a step behind him, then collapsed down to sit on it, trying to find his breath. Bill O'Neal squatted down on the curb beside him, switching the light off, revealing a lovely moonlit night, clear, stars sparkling. O'Neal quietly waited for the Judge's explanation.

The Judge settled his breathing, forced his body to release its tension, to relax, then started in. His words fell over one another as he told of his return to the maintenance room to look again at what was now a homicide crime scene. He spoke of his search for exits, of his tapping walls, of his finding the sliding paneling giving egress to the boiler room and out through the trapdoors, of the beaten-down path in the weeds. How he'd returned to the maintenance room, only to hear someone enter the boiler room. He said 'hear', not mentioning the rigged TV for surveillance because he wasn't ready to disclose his suspicions about how the old TV in the maintenance room had been used. He spoke of Narrow Eyes and the bags of pills.

O'Neal listened without interrupting, then sat quiet for a time, rolling the flashlight in his hands.

"Okay, Judge, I believe you. You don't look the sort to be involved in drugs. Are you sure it was this drug dealer guy, Jack, in there?"

"Yes."

"But he didn't use the panel door to enter the maintenance room?"

"No. He didn't need to. What he wanted was hidden in the boiler room."

"So we don't know if Jack Druggie knew about the paneled entrance?

"No. But he might have."

"Okay. A call came into the station about a prowler at The Strand about forty-five minutes ago. No doubt about you, Judge. Everyone else was tied up so I came over to investigate. Glad you weren't hurt.

And by the way, your friend, detective Oliver Hardy, is entirely off The Strand case and the Simpson case. He'll be doing traffic court for a while now after that silly stunt. Thank you for your letter. I apologize for Detective Hardy's actions."

The Judge nodded.

O'Neal continued, "You said a third bag of pills was dropped back into its hiding place when the guy fled."

"I think so."

"Let's go back and collect the gentleman's drugs."

They retraced the Judge's steps. The Judge used his cell phone light again as O'Neal retrieved the dropped bag of pills, and a second bag beneath it."

"Opioids, a thousand pills in each bag, fifty dollars per pill, gives a street value of fifty thousand to each bag," said O'Neal. "These two bags are a hundred thousand on the hoof. So, Judge, we've got a secret panel and a semi-secret room, drugs, and a murder. Do you think this alleged child molestation ring was operating here as well?"

"This is a furnace room, Bill, hardly a secret room. There is a secret panel. There was a homicide in the next room, with access. There were drugs stashed here. It's clear something elicit was going on. But none of this proves there was child molestation."

"Right, defense counsel. Just what I'd expect you to say. Why don't you get out of here? I'll tape things off here, turn in the pills, do a report, and bring in forensics for a sweep first thing in the morning. Come by tomorrow and give us a good description of your Narrow-Eyed Jack friend. Maybe we'll get a sketch artist involved."

The Judge got up and followed O'Neal out the trapdoors, closing them behind them. The Judge was too proud to ask, but O'Neal sensed what was needed, and walked the Judge to his car. The Judge climbed in and sped up Ocean Hill Drive to Pacific Coast Highway, very relieved to be away from The Strand.

CHAPTER 40

"This just in...   Last night three female inmates of the Los Angeles City jail attacked another inmate, a rather infamous one, Laura Wilson, and set her hair afire.   Recall she has red hair. It must have been a sight to see her hair go up in flames. I understand it was really 'blazing' red after that."   The reporter chuckled.

Anyway, the jailers intervened and no serious harm was done to Wilson, just crisp ends and damaged pride. Wilson was lucky, this time. But even our jailed prisoners are angry about what the Wilsons have done to those poor molested children from The Strand Pre-School."

The Judge snapped the TV off as he dove into the bathroom before Katy could get in, looking forward to a more relaxed shower and shave this morning. He heard Katy squawk a protest as he shut the door, but he'd beat her fair and square.

Two hours later the Judge suspended his huddle with Barney and the Wilsons at the defense table. Laura was physically okay, suffering only roasted hair ends from the attack, just as the news had reported. But she was emotionally shaken. Her beautiful red hair was hidden now under a white silk bandana.   Her hands shook as she grabbed the Judge's hand for support under the table, making a soft joke about never wanting to roast marshmallows again, trying to look brave.

Ferguson tramped in fifteen minutes late and the trial resumed. The prosecution called Dr Eugene Westwood to the stand. Westwood was a Los Angeles pediatrician who'd been asked by the prosecution to physically examine 150 of the current and former Strand Pre-School students.

After qualification of Westwood, Armstrong asked, "You physically examined the children who will testify in this trial, Doctor?"

"I have."

"And are you prepared to discuss your findings as a result of your exams?'

"I am."

"And what did you use to conduct these examinations, Doctor?" The Judge hated the way Armstrong sounded so smug and confident.

"I utilized a colposcope."

"And what does a colposcope do?"

"A colposcope is a relatively new device that can magnify the interior walls of the vagina and the anus to show scar tissue, or a lack thereof. The device also allows you to take pictures of these interior walls on a magnified basis."

Jay Armstrong produced grainy pictures of grey walls of various structures and waved them around with a flourish as though they were the wedding pictures of his Aunt Agnes. He finally handed them over to be marked as exhibits and then delivered them into the hands of the witness. Dr. Westlake identified the pictures as those he'd taken as part of his examination of ten of The Strand Pre-School children, using the colposcope. He identified them as pictures of each child's anus, and in the case of the girls, their vaginas.

"And what did you find from this examination with your colposcope, as documented in these photos?" Armstrong asked triumphantly.

"I found genital and rectal marking."

"Can you be more specific?"

"I found scars, tears, enlarged body openings and other physical evidence most likely demonstrating blunt-force penetrating trauma, all consistent with the repeated rape and sodomy the children have described."

"In how many of the children?"

"In ten of the children."

"And were you surprised to find so many injuries in the group of children examined?"

"Yes, I was. Sexual abuse often leaves no detectable signs, and so I was surprised to find injuries, and in some cases injuries indicative of severe trauma, in so many children."

"So, based on your expertise and your examinations, what have you concluded?"

In my professional opinion, these ten children I examined were most likely physically molested by forced penetration of their private parts."

Westwood elaborated with slides projected on a hastily erected screen, presenting the areas where he said there was trauma in each of the ten children.

On cross examination, the Judge asked questions from the defense table without getting up, implying the doctor's testimony was no big thing to the defense, not warranting his returning to his feet to pace around.

"How many children did you examine?"

"One hundred and fifty children."

"And did you find any indications of molestation in the other one hundred and forty children?"

"No. But that's not to say it didn't occur."

"But you found no proof it occurred in these one hundred and forty other children?"

"No."

"The abuse you assume from your slides, if it happened, could have taken place anywhere couldn't it, Doctor? For instance, on a city playground, or at home? And it could have occurred through interaction with someone other than the defendants, such as with relatives, with parents, with other playmates outside The Strand Pre-School grounds, even with a priest?"

"Yes, I suppose so."

"And it could have resulted from self-examination and self-manipulation, could it not?"

"Well, theoretically."

"Does that mean 'yes'?"

"Yes."

"How accurate is the colposcope, Doctor?"

"Very. You can see the pictures for yourself."

"I'm sure it's quite good at taking pictures. The questions is, what do the pictures mean? Is there universal agreement on what it means when the colposcope finds markings like you've found in these pictures, in a child's genitals or anus?"

"Well. It's a new instrument. Not all doctors are familiar with the colposcope's use."

"You're saying there is no universal agreement among members of your profession as to what these markings mean?"

"Well, 'universal' would mean every single doctor in my area of specialty agrees, and of course…"

"Don't be coy, Doctor. Isn't it a further fact that current research estimates that perhaps fifty percent of all children have similar markings as a matter of congenital conditions unrelated to child molestation?"

"There are some estimates like that."

"So how can you render any professional opinion with certainty that these markings were made by forced penetration?"

"I said 'most likely' made."

"But if an estimated fifty percent of such marking are the result of a congenital condition, not penetration, and if there are all kinds of ways these markings could have occurred without third party penetration, how can you say it's 'more likely' caused by penetration?"

"Well, that might be a slight overstatement."

"No further questions."

Ferguson then called a halt to the proceedings for the day. The defense team said goodbye to their clients and trudged out of the courtroom. Barney and the Judge were tired. It had been a grueling day. They made the way down the long hall, threading their way through a crowd of litigants, attorneys, witnesses and newly called jurors, some looking scared, some looking angry, some looking crafty, most looking bored, to the elevator, to the lobby, and down the outside stairs to the street, dodging reporters, photographers, microphones, and muttering repeatedly, "no comment."

CHAPTER 41

The Judge watched the patrons in the bar with interest, despite them being twenty-five years his junior. They were packed into Shucky's like sardines. He'd been on the way home from court, but for the hell of it he'd detoured to the bar on the Hermosa Pier. He toyed with the idea of a second drink while he relaxed and watched the flora and fauna, hard-toned female bodies trawling for permanence amongst a potpourri of males of varying sizes, wallets and intentions. Mostly short-term in intent.

Katy was off at a school counselors' meeting this evening. Only the dog would be at home right now. To hell with it. He sent two fingers into the air, circling, attracting the attention of a pretty young girl, college age, dressed in a black spandex material that looked to belong in a gym. It covered everything, and for all of that it was so sheer and tight it covered nothing, leaving no room for imagination. She apparently didn't believe in undergarments. It was all very enjoyable. Even old guys can dream.

He ordered a second Dos Equis and then stood up, threading his way through the throng to the toilet to take a whizz. The men's and women's toilet shared a common wash room, the men's john decked out in

288

checkered black and white tile, reminding the Judge of a New York subway toilet, smelling of fresh pissed beer and sickly sweet deodorize. Native Americana in the 21st Century.

Returning to his table his beer was sitting there, along with a check. He glanced at it, noting the waitress had stiffed him for an extra drink. It was continuing to be one of those days. He sighed, then laid cash on the table to cover the bill and a reasonable tip. He settled into his seat, downing a couple of slugs of the Dos Equis. It was his favorite brew, although there was a slight tinny taste to it tonight. He hadn't noticed that before.

A buxom blonde had turned on her stool at the bar and was giving him the eye, a little older than much of the crowd, perhaps mid-thirties, still way younger than the Judge. He basked in the attention, straightening a little in his seat, trying to look distinguished, pleased to be noted. The girl obviously knew quality.

But after a while when he made no move to get up, she turned back to the bar, disappointed, disinterested. Although he didn't wear a wedding ring, disliking jewelry of all sorts except for his Rolex, he supposed there was a sense about him that said married, or at least committed. So much of the communication between members of the human species was still animal based, small inflections and movements conveying interest and availability, or not.

Suddenly he was dizzy, very dizzy. The room swam around him, even though he was sitting still. His face felt flush and it was difficult to breathe. He hoisted himself up, his legs wobbly, supporting himself with the table for a second, then waddled his way through the crowd, bumping startled guests here and there in a rush for the back door of Shucky's and fresh air.

He made it out and it helped a little. But the dizziness was coming in spasms now, gradually increasing. He plunged ahead toward his car parked in the dark lot fifty feet away, finding it difficult to keep his balance. If he could only reach his car he could rest inside. There was no way he could drive.

He slammed into his driver's side door like a runaway tug and, holding himself up against it, wildly fumbled to get the keys out of his pocket. Instinct made him look up, briefly focusing on the shape of a man, younger, muscular, motorcycle helmet on his head, dark green visor pulled down, approaching. There was something about the man… what was it? … menace.

Then he saw the knife, a switchblade fully extended at the man's side. The guy was walking up quickly now, head swinging to either side, confirming no one else was around.

Pushing the 'open' button on his key fob with what was left of his fast disappearing clarity, he scrambled into the car and locked the doors with one motion, then pressed his fingers to the horn and held it there with all his might. The blaring horn seemed to rattle inside his skull as he held the horn down with what was left of his rapidly failing strength. Hold… Hold…Hold…*Ohhhh…*

Everything went black.

Groggy, he tried to raise his head sometime later, disturbed by a rapping close to his ear. He opened one eye, the only one which seemed to work, then closed it immediately, searing pain stabbing through his head from the bright light shown into his face.

More rapping. He wished the rapping would go away. More rapping. Finally, he managed to locate a hand and make it work to move over his face, shielding his eyes while he opened one eye again experimentally, then the other.

He peeked out, waving away at the bright light with his other hand. The painful light was withdrawn. He could see some now. There was a black shape, black leather, with a shiny badge on it, and then a face above, bending down, peering at him through the door's side window. More rapping. Motions to open the window.

He tried the window button. Nothing happened. The key... the key in the ignition was in the off position. He reached over and turned it on, then hit the window button to lower it.

"Are you okay, sir?" The cop learned in through his window to get a good sniff of the Judge's breath. He was glad he didn't have to sniff people's breath all evening as a job. The thought made him giggle, but he clamped his jaws shut as the cop's face turned stern.

"Are you sure you're okay, sir?"

He hated to be called 'sir' by younger men. A painful reminder of how old he'd become. He could see more clearly now. This cop didn't look old enough to shave.

"I don't think I can drive," he muttered.

"No. I think not." The cop leaned in again, his light darting now about the car, front seat, back seat, floor boards, looking for contraband.

"Is there someone you can call? Or do you want to Uber home?"

"I'll call an Uber, leave the car here if I can," said the Judge, his senses beginning to clear.

"Someone reported you were leaning on your horn. Thought it might be an emergency. You sure you're okay?"

"I'm okay."

"Are you on drugs?"

"Not that I know of."

"What'd you have to drink?"

"Two beers."

"Recently?"

The Judge looked at his watch. "About forty-five minutes ago, I left Shucky's. I consumed two beers over perhaps an hour there. I'm not drunk."

"You don't look too good."

"It may be a touch of food poisoning."

"You want me to call the paramedics?"

"No. I'm better now. Much better."

"You're sure?"

"Yes."

"Can I see your license and registration?"

It was a test; the Judge could sense it. He wearily got the registration out of the glove compartment, then fumbled with his wallet and produced his license. The white light came back on, but thankfully this time stayed on his documents.

The police radio on the cop's shoulder suddenly squawked a code and an address. The officer's head came up sharply, suddenly in a hurry.

"Okay, sir. I'm not writing you up," he said, starting to turn, anxious to leave. "It's early still, only nine p.m.," he shouted over his shoulder, moving briskly back toward his vehicle. "No more beer. Uber home or call someone. Don't want to see you driving."

The police car swung backward quickly, then roared out of the parking lot. The Judge got out of his car, stretched and looked around. No one was lurking in the parking lot. He made his way back across the lot and through the back door into Shucky's and found an empty stool at the bar next to the buxom blonde still there and happy to see him. He ordered a coffee, black.

Did a motorcycled guy just come after him with a knife, or was it all a nightmare? He wasn't sure. It was all mixed up.

What the hell just happened?

CHAPTER 42

The next morning the Judge arrived early, traffic being light and settled into the defense table well ahead of the defendants and Barney. Laura was escorted in and took her seat beside the Judge, taking his hand with a grip of desperation, sliding the length of her thigh against his under the table for warmth and support. She looked very tired under her pancake makeup which couldn't hide the wreckage, dark circles under her eyes, gaunt from weight loss, her attempted smile more like a grimace. Her scarlet curls were still hidden under the white bandana which was more droopy this morning. She slumped more than sat in her chair at the defense table.

The prosecution began the morning proceedings by calling the first child witness. Carley was six, a tiny little thing. She made her way through the courtroom and up the big step to the raised platform, all curls and freckles in a scotch plaid dress. The Clerk helped her with the second-high step to climb up to the witness box, placing a pillow on the seat under her to raise her high enough so she could peek over its rail, flushed and wide eyed.

"Tell us what happened at The Strand Pre-School?" droned Jay Armstrong, solicitous like a smarmy minister, after extracting her name, age, and years of attendance at the school.

"They made me play the Naked Movie Star game."

"How was that game played, Carley?"

"The kids took all their clothes off and danced around."

"And you took off all your clothes, Carly?"

"Yes." Carly's voice was so soft now one could hardly hear her.

"You and your classmates?"

"Yes."

"Who made you play the Naked Movie Star game?"

"Mr. Harry. Miss Laura."

"Are Mr. Harry and Miss Laura in the courtroom here right now? Can you point at them with your finger?"

A small hand was thrust out, the finger unclutching from a fist, the index finger ranging the room, then settling on the defense table. Then Carley shut her eyes, fearful.

"Were other adult people there too when you played the game?"

"Sometimes."

"Do you know who they were?"

"No."

"Did they take pictures?"

"Yes, everyone took pictures."

"Of you?"

"Yes."

"Without clothes?"

"Yes."

"Of the other kids playing the game?"

"Yes."

"Did Mr. Harry and Miss Laura make you play the game?"

"Yes… Well, kinda."

"Did you want to play the game?"

"Well. No. It's kinda naughty."

"How did they make you play the game?"

"Mr. Harry killed a cat. He said it could happen to us if we didn't do as we were told."

"He did that and said that in front of all the kids?"

"Yes."

"How did Mr. Harry kill the cat?"

"With a knife. He stabbed it." Carley stuck her small fist out over the witness box rail and made a thrusting motion down with it, a serious look on her face.

"Did anyone touch you when you played this game?"

"Yes."

"Who?"

"Mr. Harry, with his fingers."

"Where did he touch you?"

"Down here." Carley pointed to her tummy, hidden by the rail of the witness box.

"In your private parts?"

"Yes."

"Did Mr. Wilson say anything when he killed the cat?"

"Yes. He said it could happen to me and my mom if I told."

"You played the Naked Movie Star game at school?"

"Yes."

"Did you play it anywhere else?

"At a house."

"Do you know where the house was?"

"No. But it was a farm house."

"Were you given any medicine before you played these naked games?"

"Yes. A pink medicine."

"How did you feel after taking the pink medicine?"

"Drowsy"

"No further questions."

The Judge unwound himself from his seat at the defense table like a coiled spring, popping up and striding toward the witness box to lean near the little witness.

"That's quite a story, Carley. And a lot to remember."

"Yes."

"And you say you were given a pink medicine, and it made you drowsy?"

"Yes."

"How it is you can remember so clearly all that happened if you were so drowsy?"

"I don't know. I just do."

"Did Mr. Armstrong help you remember what happened?"

"Yes."

"Did you practice? Mr. Armstrong asking questions. You answering his questions?"

Carly looked around over to where Armstrong was sitting, sudden concern spreading across her face.

"Carly, you have to listen to me now and truthfully answer the questions. You can't look at Mr. Armstrong for help."

"Okay."

"Did you practice Mr. Armstrong asking questions, you answering Mr. Armstrong's questions, before now?"

"Yes."

"Did he tell you what to answer?"

"No."

"Did he remind you what you'd said before, when you talked about this before in your interview with Mr. Gibson?"

"Yes."

"Did he help you recall what you said before? What your answers were supposed to be?"

"Yes. He told me the 'smart' answers."

"He gave you your 'smart answers'?"

"Yes."

"Because you couldn't remember so well?"

"Yes."

"So, you practiced your 'smart answers' with Mr. Armstrong?"

"Yes."

"No further questions."

The next witness was a five-year-old girl, Lindy, clearly terrified by the courtroom, all the people staring at her, and thundering Judge Ferguson sitting above her in his black robes with a perpetual scowl, pounding his gavel periodically. Jay Armstrong bustled around in front of her proprietarily, towering over her even though he stood on the floor and she was up in the witness box. She looked like she might be sick.

"Have you ever been touched by any of the adults at The Strand School in private places?" Armstrong asked.

The girl nodded with big eyes.

"You have to speak your answer, Lindy. If your answer is yes, then you have to say 'Yes'."

A soft little voice whispered "yes" from the witness box.

"Can you tell us where?"

"Front and back," the child whispered.

"In your private parts?"

"Yes."

"And this happen at The Strand Pre-School?"

"Yes."

"Did it happen anywhere else?'

"Yes. At a farm house, at a car wash, and at a market." This last was said in a rush.

"What else happened at these places?"

"People took pictures while we played naked games."

"The Naked Movie Star game?"

"Yes."

"You and the other kids?"

"Yes."

"No further questions."

The Judge slumped in his seat, apparently thinking. Then he seemed to recover quickly, leaping up and walking with slow measured steps to the witness stand. He did enjoy a bit of drama. Close to the witness box, he suddenly pivoted toward Judge Ferguson.

"Your honor, I'd like to play an excerpt from the video tape of Miss Lindy's interview by Gibson to the jury."

Armstrong leaped to his feet, stumbling over his words in his heat to object to this request. After bitter argument between the attorneys, the Judge ruled the tape could be shown as part of cross examination, and sixty seconds later the courtroom went dark, all eyes on the screen that slid down from the ceiling.

The video showed Gibson interviewing Lindy. He gave Lindy a hand puppet, Rags the Racoon, to put on her hand, as a device to help her answer his questions.

"The other children have already told me some yucky secrets, Lindy. They've told me that the teachers are all sick in the head and deserved to be beaten up. Now, I need your help in figuring out what happened at the school, or what might have happened, when the children were touched."

Lindy looked at Gibson, wide-eyed.

"Think Mr. Harry might have done some of the touching?"

Lindy shook her head 'no'.

Gibson turned slightly to address her handheld puppet. "Where do you think he would have touched her, Rags? Can you use the pointer, Rags, and show where he would have touched her?"

Gibson picked up and placed under Lindy's nose a female doll, nude, with realistic genital parts. He then produced a pencil and put it in Rags' mouth, Rags still on Lindy's hand.

Gibson: "Can you show us where he might have touched her, Rags? Go on, just point with the pencil, Rags."

Lindy shrugged and had Rags point at the doll's head.

Gibson: "Where else?"

Rags pointed at an arm.

Gibson: "Where else, Rags?"

Rags pointed to the other arm.

Gibson: "Where else?"

Lindy appeared to get frustrated. Rags pointed at the backside of the doll.

Gibson: "Good, very good, Rags. Now we're getting somewhere. Where else?"

Lindy had Rags point to the doll's genitals.

Gibson: "Very good. Very good."

Gibson produced from the box behind him a male doll, nude, also with realistic genitals.

Gibson: "What part of Mr. Harry would have touched her do you think, Rags?"

Again, Rags pointed to the head of the doll.

After further urging and several tries, Rags pointed to the male doll's genitals.

The Judge stood as the screen silently disappeared into the ceiling.

"Your Honor, the defense asks this witnesses' testimony be struck in its entirety as it was clearly testimony fabricated by Gibson, b using his technique of leading the child to the predetermined result he wanted to obtain.

"Motion denied. Let's move it along, gentlemen."

The next witness was a five-year-old boy, also nervous, one Joseph Wood.

"Tell me, Joe, what sort of games did you play at The Strand Pre-School?" asked Armstrong.

"We played Cowboys and Indians."

"How did you play Cowboys and Indians?"

"We kids are the cowboys. We take off our clothes. The teachers are the Indians. They make a circle around us and take pictures."

"What other games did you play at The Strand?"

"Well, we played the Alligator Game."

"And how do you play the Alligator Game?"

"We kids take off all our clothes and crawl around the floor and the teachers touched us."

"Can you think of any other game that you played?"

"We played the Naked Movie Star game. That's where we kids take off our clothes and get photographed and we sing a song."

"Can you sing the song for us, Joe?"

Joe launched into song in a high thin voice.

"What you see… is what you are… you're a Naked… Movie Star."

"Were there other games?"

302

Yes. In 'TICKLE', we kids take off our clothes and the teachers tickle us in the butt and on our privates."

"Are the teachers at The Strand who played these games here in the courtroom today?"

"Yes sir."

"Can you point them out to the Court?"

"Over there." He pointed to the defense table, to Laura Wilson and Harry Wilson.

"Where did these teachers touch you, Joe?"

"On my penis and on my butt."

"Did that hurt?"

"Yes."

"Did anyone photograph you while this touching was going on?"

"Yes."

"Who photographed you?"

Miss Laura touched me, and Mr. Harry took pictures. Then Mr. Harry touched me, and Miss Laura took pictures."

On cross examination, Barney stood up and approached close to the young witness, smiling.

"Did Mr. Armstrong tell you to say Harry Wilson touched you on the penis and butt, Joe?"

Joe gulped, "He helped me remember, yes."

"You said Laura Wilson watched you kids playing these games. Why was that?"

"It was what I remembered."

"You mean what Mr. Armstrong helped you remember?"

"Yes."

"You're just telling the story that Mr. Armstrong wants you to tell, aren't you Joe? The story that Doctor Gibson wants you to tell. The story that your mom and dad want you to tell?"

"Yes sir. I'm a good boy."

"But we have to have the truth here, Joe. We have to know only what you really saw with your own eyes. And what you really remember about it. Think carefully now, Joe." Barney paused for a fifteen-beat count. Do you specifically remember Miss Laura Wilson photographing you?"

"No."

"Do you specifically remember Miss Laura Wilson touching your privates?"

"No."

"Do you specifically remember Mr. Harry Wilson photographing you?"

"No."

"Do you specifically remember Mr. Harry Wilson touching your private parts?"

"No."

"No further questions."

Armstrong brought a young man named Sam to the stand next. Sam declared he was now five years old, and testified he'd gone on field trips from The Strand Pre-School. On these trips Sam testified he'd been photographed naked by the defendants and by other adults, and he'd been touched by the defendants and other adults on his penis and his butt.

Rising for cross examination, the Judge produced a large poster on which he'd glued the photos of several people. He produced a folding tripod stand from his brief case and, unfolding it, placed the chart on the stand, and the stand angled so both Sam and the jury could see.

"Sam, I've got here a series of pictures of adults other than the defendants who may have participated in these naked games you so vividly recall playing on these field trips from The Strand Pre-School."

Armstrong jumped to his feet, his voice going falsetto as he screeched, "Objection! Objection!", his mouth running over with reasons the question couldn't or shouldn't be asked."

"Overruled."

"As you can see, Sam, I have ten pictures of adults here on my poster. Do you recognize any of these people as the other adults who took pictures of you naked, or touched you in private places, while on field trips from The Strand Pre-School? Look carefully now, Sam, and take your time. I want you to be sure. Can you identify with certainty that any of these people were present and participated in these naked games you've described?"

"Yes, sir. That man there, the man there, the man there, and the lady there." Sam used his finger to point to various pictures on the poster.

"My that's quite a number I got right on my poster, Sam. Each of these people attended these parties, and observed or touched you and your fellow students after you'd all taken off your clothes?"

Sam nodded.

"Is that a 'yes' Sam?"

"Yes."

"You're sure, Sam?"

"Yes."

The Judge turned to look up at Ferguson. "Let the record show that Sam has identified with certainty as a part of his molesters, a Los Angeles City Attorney, a famous movie actor, a congressman, and a nun, none of whom have any connection with The Strand Pre-School or the defendants."

"Objection... Objection... Objection..." Armstrong was sputtering again, almost hopping up and down with agitation.

"Overruled."

There were originally thirteen children listed to testify at the trial. But in the middle of the proceeding four children were withdrawn by their parents from testifying. The four parents all said the same thing. They would not expose their child to the trauma of appearing, testifying, and being cross examined. Nor would they subject their child to the screaming media waiting outside like angry hornets at the steps to the courthouse, ready to swoop down upon any young person seen leaving the courthouse while the trial was underway.

As a result, the prosecutor had to drop many of charges originally filed. The Judge could almost hear Armstrong grinding his teeth as he doubled down on the fifty-two counts remaining.

During the following five days, the prosecution called each of the remaining nine children to the stand to answer Armstrong's questions. And then to face cross-examination from each of the two defending lawyers, and re-cross by Armstrong. The result was an exhausting experience for the witnesses and for everybody in the courtroom. As the children got tired on the stand, their testimony grew hazier and often became inconsistent. Either with their earlier testimony, or with their videotaped interviews, or with their initial testimony to the grand jury.

Various children testified to various things, including being tied up, locked in a closet, posed naked for photographs, being touched, rubbed up against, and sexually abused. There was testimony that the defendants and other adults wearing black robes and masks danced around the children, singing and moaning. There was testimony of molestation at a farm house, in the back room of a local market, at a car wash, in a secret room at the school, at a church, and under the apple tree in the adjacent vacant lot. There was testimony of killing small animals to scare the children into silence, and accounts of digging up bodies at a cemetery to mutilate.

Some children had said 'no' when initially asked in the Gibson interviews if they'd been touched in private places, or said they didn't remember, or said they didn't know. They later reversed their testimony. Others had said at the preliminary hearing they'd taken off their clothes but not been touched, and now said they had been touched. The children were very suggestible. A line of defense questioning about what they said they remembered on the first day of testimony, would often lead to the child not remembering when asked the same or a similar question on the second day of testimony."

Barney and the Judge asked minute details of rooms, people and rituals, pouncing on any discrepancies from earlier testimony from the Gibson interviews, the Grand Jury testimony, and the preliminary hearing testimony of the children. Barney argued that only after heavy coaching by the prosecution and an emphasis on 'smart answers', had the children changed their stories and declared they'd been touched in their private parts.

The defense couldn't shake the testimony of most of the children witnesses, but they extracted and pointed out discrepancies and inconsistencies from earlier statements which the children couldn't explain.

At the conclusion of the children's testimony the Judge rose to say, "Your honor. I request that the testimony of all of these children be stricken from the evidence, as unreliable, uncorroborated, inconsistent, and the result of illegal prepping by the district attorney."

Armstrong shot up like a rocket, protesting.

The Judge banged his gavel several times to shut down the argument that quickly degenerated into an unseemly verbal exchange between lawyers.

"Counsel, Counsel. Please sit down. The objection of defense counsel is overruled. This case will proceed with the defense putting on its case next. We are adjourned for the day."

Smash went the gavel.

CHAPTER 43

"The disturbing testimony of the young witnesses in The Strand Pre-School Wilson trial was painful to listen to. These poor children. One young child said Harry Wilson had sodomized him orally and anally in the pre-school bathroom; another boy said he and a group of children were taken to a car wash where they were molested one by one in the bathroom; still others said they had been raped in the back room of a meat market. Some also described games of "Naked Movie Star" and "Tickle," in which they said they were forced to undress and then were fondled by the Wilsons or made to perform sex acts while being photographed.

The Judge slammed the TV off in the kitchen with one hand, balancing two pieces of toast loaded with berry jam in the other, fumbling at the last minute and almost losing the toast to the floor. Annie the Dog was there waiting, hopeful, like some alligator lurking under a bridge, hoping or a spill. The Judge wouldn't normally have loaded the jelly on so heavy, but Katy was already gone. Besides, he was now running late too.

A half hour later the Judge walked into the Earthen Pot Coffee Bar in the downtown strip of Ocean Hill Boulevard, and asked for the manager. He'd been tipped the manager was the new fiancé of Louisa Simpson, now Louisa McFarland, Jeffrey's ex-wife. The man that walked out around the counter to shake his hand looked personable, friendly, and clean cut. Six-foot-three, hazel eyes and a bland smile. He exuded the kind polish two years of business school will give. Early thirties, he wore blue scrubbed jeans and a checked blue sport shirt, hidden for the most part by the de rigeur green apron.

"I'm Sean Black. How can I help you, sir?"

Damn, there was that sir again, like he was an old man. The Judge took a deep breath and tried to coax his ruffled feathers down, accepting the proffered hand and using his mature willpower not to crush it. The guy's handshake was strike two against him, limp like a wet rag. They didn't teach them much at UCLA.

"I'm new to the area," said the Judge, "and a friend of my family, Louis McFarland, said you might give me a little insight into Ocean Hill as a good place to settle."

"Love to," said Black, "Louisa is the best damn real estate agent in California. You can't go wrong using her," making the connection between his girlfriend's business and the Judge's request. "Let's sit out on the patio, I'll provide the coffee."

They sat in the sun at a small table and watched the hoi polloi of Ocean Hill go by, young moms in spandex jogging by solo, on bikes, or pushing baby carriages, tight tan bodies, a high proportion of blonds, natural and otherwise. Out for a stroll or a jog at this hour was a clear sign they had settled here with rich hubbies, off to work somewhere pushing the wheel to support the beach lifestyle. Black's soliloquy on the area finally wound down after a while, allowing the Judge to ask some questions.

"How do you like working for the Earthen Pot Coffee Bar, Sean?"

"It's a great company, Judge. A great place to start my new career in this industry. Course I'm in management, so this store manager job is just for a few months to learn the business. Then they'll move me up to a middle position in marketing. That's what my master's is in."

"So, you'll stay with the company?" The Judge's friendly eyes focused on Sean, a warm smile of interest on his face.

"Interesting you should ask, Judge. Perhaps Louisa mentioned it. Our real plan is to open my own store, and very soon. Louisa and I are going to be partners. She's going to have capital to fund a purchase of an existing facility we can upgrade. We're searching now for a store to buy."

"That's great, Sean. Congratulations. How long has this been in planning?"

"About eight weeks.

"Are you looking for investors? I might know someone who would invest."

"What a great idea. You really think you might know someone?"

"I might. How much will you and Louisa be putting in?"

"About $750,000, Louisa's money, as soon as it comes through. But if we had another, say, $200,000, we could do some real promotion and bring the store to positive cash flow very quickly."

"I'll follow up with my friend." Said the Judge, thinking to himself the $750,000 was Louisa's insurance policy on Jeffrey's life. But predicting it eight weeks back, she must have an uncanny ability to predict the future.

Sean was all smiles now, his attention directed to some different time and space in the future and his fantasy of what life would be like. The Judge wondered how accurate his fantasy about Louisa McFarland would be once they were married and she'd funded his business.

"Is Louisa related to that guy I was just reading about? The Simpson guy that killed himself at some pre-school?"

Sean snapped out of his fantasy with a start, his eyes narrowing in suspicion. Then he relaxed.

"No, I don't think so." He lied. "That's an old name from a long-ago marriage. She just still uses the name occasionally."

The Judge stood, thanked Sean Black for the coffee and the perspective on Ocean Hill and walked back to his car just as the parking meter was about to expire. He, jumping ahead of the meter-made, two cars down, and began the track further north to Venice and his law office. There was a pile of cleanup work awaiting him there..

Late that afternoon as the sun dropped close to the horizon, spilling a soft orange haze out on the edge of the great Santa Monica Bay, the Judge pulled into the driveway of his Palos Verdes villa and paused in his convertible for a moment, admiring the sea, its surface rippled in constant motion, sending a wide arc of white foam sliding up the beaches below.

It was so peaceful. He never tired of the constantly changing sky and sea, stretched out below him like some mosaic seascape. As he reached over to the passenger seat to retrieve his file of work, he was startled by a soft plopping sound, his eyes widening at the splintered hole which suddenly appeared in his passenger side window. He vaguely felt the splinter of plastic and leather as a second plop was accompanied by something burying itself into the car's arm rest at his left.

"*Shit.*"

It was a gunshot.

CHAPTER 44

He instinctively huddled down in the seat as a third pop came with the sound of shattering glass, this time his entire passenger side window disintegrated.

Staying low, he scrambled out of the driver's door and slumped to the ground, his back against the driver's door. He was panicked, uncertain which way to move. He reached in through the open car door and snatched his cell phone from the center console, fingers fumbling in his urgent effort to dial 9-1-1.

"They're shooting at me," he gasped into the phone, his voice sounding strange and hoarse.

"What's your location?"

He rattled off his address, wondering if he should stay put or make a run for the house.

"Officers are on the way. What's your name?"

His voice broke in response, finally forcing his name out.

"What's your situation."

He went through the details. Crouched now behind his car, uncertain what to do. He could hear sirens in the distance, more than one.

"Do you see anyone?"

"No. Shall I peek?"

"No. Stay down. If you didn't see anyone, they're probably some distance away; it will be difficult to work around for a clear shot on the other side of your vehicle. Besides, officers will be there in about a minute and a half. I'd stay put."

"Okay."

Suddenly his front door opened at the upper end of his driveway and Katy walked out onto their porch, her hand shading her eyes from the setting sun so she could better see what was going on.

"Judge! Judge! What're you up to? Why are you sitting on the driveway?"

"Stay back, Katy!"

"You're not hurt are you, Judge? Not having something silly like a heart attack? You're going to get your pants dirty. Shall I call auto club?"

She was standing on her tiptoes now at the edge of the porch to see better, presenting an even better target.

"Stay back, Katy. Stay back!" he screeched. "There's a shooter out here somewhere. For God sakes get back in the house and lock the door. I've called the police."

Katy's face went puzzled. "I can't make you out, Judge. Are you hurt? I'll come see."

"No, No, Katy. This is an active shooter. Get back in the house." The Judge lifted his hands, palms outward, and desperately pushed them away toward the house. "Go back, damn it. Go back inside."

"Are you hurt?"

Jesus, she loved to use her words. Why couldn't she just take direction and move quickly?

He shouted again, "No. Not hurt. Just scared. Scared for you."

"Can't make you out, Judge. Shall I send the dog? She wants to help, whatever it is."

The dog? The golden retriever? Annie? She'd probably lick his assailant to death, demanding attention and perhaps a treat. It was such an absurd idea he smiled despite himself, then he giggled, then he broke into laughter.

Katy's eyes got bigger, wondering what she'd said, why her husband was laughing like a maniac, crouched behind his car on the ground, getting his slacks dirty, flinging his arms around at her like some Whirling Dervish. She still hadn't gone back in the house. Stubborn! Jesus, he was afraid she would be hit.

The street below his driveway was suddenly filled with screaming sirens and flashing lights, two police cars pulling in together in tandem, barricading access to his driveway, cops scrambling out to crouch behind their cars, drawing guns, eyes swinging in 360 degrees, uncertain what they'd driven into. A third car came wobbling up the street from the other direction, the officer leaping out and scrambling for his trunk, whipping out a shotgun and then crouching behind his car.

"Are you okay, Judge?" called one of the policemen.

"I'm not hit, just shaken up, but would you tell my idiot wife to go back inside and lock her door."

Katy snorted from their porch. She apparently heard that just fine.

One of the cops turned to look at the Judge, questioningly. "Is this a domestic dispute, Judge?"

CHAPTER 45

Soon a perimeter was established, a drone was produced out of a cruiser's trunk and sent aloft to scan the brush on the opposite hillside, the apparent direction from which the shot had come, and later a copter arrived, swooping low to inspect the surrounding terrain. No one was found. The police finally declared things safe and secure. The Judge slowly made his way up his driveway to the safety of his porch and his bride. Katy had locked Ralphie in his room with Annie the Dog for protection, and then returned to the living room to anxiously watch the scene play out through their large viewing window..

She gave him a big hug and a smooch on the cheek, then buried her head in his shoulder, whispering, "I'm so glad you weren't hurt."

His irritation with her evaporated, replaced by the warmth of her body which seemed to flow through him and generate renewed energy.

The next morning was a bright sunny day. The Judge noted the rays of golden sun spilling down over the courthouse steps, casting the horizontal risers in deep shadow, like rungs one had to mount to find justice in L.A.

The Judge settled at the defense table next to Laura and cranked his head around to watch the crowd file in. People were tense. The audience, mostly news people, already had strong views about what had actually happened and as to whether the defendants were guilty. The Judge only hoped the jury was open minded.

The first witness the Judge called was a medical expert to rebut the testimony of the prosecution's doctor. Because of the widespread press coverage, and the way the press had tried and convicted the defendants with their ceaseless barrage of information, some factual, some not, it had been difficult to find a practicing doctor willing to testify for the defense. The Judge wished their medical expert was a practicing doctor in California, but no one in the state would touch their case.

Barney had finally found a qualified doctor who would testify. Doctor Samuel Flint was the London City Chief Coroner and worked at the University of London Hospital. He was a well-known consultant on forensic medicine in the UK and had vast experience with child molestation.

A small man in an inexpensive brown tweed suit, a bullet shape to his head and a clipped, Hitler style, mustache, he didn't look the part of a big time doctor and medical expert. But he had a blunt way of speaking, likely from his Scottish roots, that carried well to a listener and conveyed long experience and an ability to communicate precisely what he intended, no more, no less, with conviction and integrity. The more the Judge listened to him, the more the Judge liked him.

Once ensconced on the stand by Barney and properly qualified as a medical expert with considerable experience in diagnosing abuse and molestation in young children, Dr. Flint testified he'd reviewed the medical records and anatomical slides of the children produced by Dr. Eugene Westwood with great care and studied Westwood's expert testimony given as a part of the prosecution's case.

"And did you find evidence of child molestation or abuse in these children as a result of your study of these records and slides?" asked Barney.

"For the most part I found no evidence to suggest molestation."

"You have seen Dr. Westwood's report and findings as a result of his review of these materials?"

"I have."

"And what do you say to his conclusion there was physical evidence that at least ten of the children were molested?"

"In my opinion Dr. Westwood was either mistaken, or negligent. I will add that there is substantial disagreement among physicians about how to diagnose sexual abuse and in many cases you cannot tell either way. But based on my review, I found evidence of molestation in only two of the ten alleged victims."

The defense next called Dr. Janice Towns to testify. She was qualified as a political psychologist and professor of psychiatry at the USC School of Medicine. She stated she had evaluated hundreds of alleged victims of child sexual abuse.

"Dr. Towns, what did you do to prepare for your testimony here today?" asked the Judge.

"I have reviewed all of the interview video tapes of the children who attended The Stand Pre-School and who were interviewed by Dr. George Gibson."

"These are the interview tapes of the children which have been placed into evidence in this trial?"

"Yes."

"And you've reviewed all of them?"

"Yes. I have also examined the testimony of Dr. George Gibson given at this trial and have considered his opinions drawn from his interviews and interaction with the children."

"And what is your professional opinion about the accuracy of the allegations made by the children in those tapes?"

"In my opinion, the children's statements in those interviews about what happened to them at The Strand Pre-School were so contaminated by Dr. Gibson's interviewing techniques, that whatever the children said about sexual molestation would be and is invalid and unreliable. Dr. Gibson produced a vast majority of his own verbal output, creating his own blind spot as a result."

"Could you elaborate?"

"Dr. Gibson's technique was essentially to create a script, a predetermined program imposed on the children. Because the same interview script was used for all the children, revelations of child abuse were preprogrammed in a way to generate similar responses from each.

The very concept of using a program or script in an interview of a child is wrong. Such an approach is putting into the interview situation, material from the interviewer, rather than obtaining spontaneous information from the child."

"What is your professional opinion on the use of anatomically correct dolls to elicit information from the children?"

"The problem with the dolls is their use was solely to identify the sexual body parts. At that point in the interview the children have said zero about their own sexual experiences. But they have now been directed to talk about or point to genitalia and other so-called private parts. The interviewer has essentially set the stage for the sort of response he is going to get. You've taken the children away from their own spontaneous remarks about sex and their experiences at The Strand and substituted expected and often supplied responses which come from the interviewer.

For example, Laura Wilson was introduced as an extraordinarily tall blonde female with large breasts and was called Miss Piggy at the start of the interview. Harry Wilson was identified as a roughhewed doll and introduced to the child as a bad person who needed to be put in jail. In effect Dr. Gibson presented predetermined information to the children, presented as if they were all pieces of the puzzle of what happened at the school. This technique motivated the child to solve a puzzle within the preprogrammed contexts presented by the interviewer.

This motivation can also be seen in statements like 'Are you smart or dumb?', 'Are you a good detective?', 'Are you going to please your mother and father?', and other phrases promising approval for certain responses and disapproval for responses that did not fall in line with Gibson's predetermined narrative. Dr. Gibson motivated and encouraged the child to find a solution from the information he'd already presented. As a result, the interviewer lost any spontaneous reflections the child might have had of anything that might have happened."

"No further questions."

Armstrong jumped up for cross, his cheeks pink, holding in with difficulty the outburst he dearly wanted to blast at Dr. Janice Towns. Towns looked at him calmly, fully prepared to support her opinions as required.

"Dr. Towns, you didn't personally interview any of the children, did you?"

"No."

"Don't you think the best way of determining if a child has been molested is to have a physical interview with them?"

"Of course."

"So how can you conclude that none of the children were molested if you haven't personally interviewed them?" Armstrong turned to the jury with this question, his hands on his hips, a smug look on his face.

"I haven't reached any such conclusion, Mr. Armstrong. All I've opined to is that anything these children said in the interviews conducted by Dr. Gibson, for which I have reviewed the videotaped interviews, are entirely worthless, have no probative value in this trial, and should be disregarded, due to the faulty techniques of Dr. Gibson."

"No further questions."

The Judge got up for redirect.

"Dr. Towns, you've given your professional opinion that Dr. Gibson inserted his own scenario of what happened to each child at The Strand, in the process of his interview."

"Yes."

"He emphasized his scenario, and through leading questions and other strategies, encouraged the child to adopt it, and encouraged the child to manufacture statements to confirm his scenario in the interview."

"Yes. I think that's fair."

"Dr. Towns, in your professional opinion, is it possible that Dr. Gibson's technique has as a result, planted in the child false memories of what happened, memories of events which the child may well now believe did happened, while in fact such events never occurred?"

"Yes, I believe that's quite likely, actually, given the young age of these children."

"No further questions."

Armstrong leaped to his feet again.

"Dr. Towns, you don't know whether these children are giving testimony in this trial about events that never occurred to them, do you?"

"No."

"And doctor, you don't know whether these children are giving testimony in this trial about events that were somehow manufactured into their head by Dr. Gibson, do you?"

"No. I can only state that what the children said in the taped interviews has no useful value because of the distorted techniques used by Dr. Gibson."

"No further questions."

Barney spent the balance of the day bringing various character witnesses in who testified that Laura Wilson and Harry Wilson were respectable, upstanding people. At the end of the day the defense rested its presentation of the defendants' case and the court was adjourned. Both the Judge and Barney were exhausted, along with the jury, Armstrong and Ferguson. Even the news crowd filling the courtroom, usually the hardiest of any bunch, looked wilted.

CHAPTER 46

The following morning was a Saturday and the Judge slept in; a day off from the trial. He'd turned off the damn TV alarm the night before and slept blissfully late. He dreamt he was preparing to shave, coating his jaw from a soft shaving brush loaded with warm sticky shaving cream, smearing it all over his chin and up his cheeks. It felt warm, and sensual and clean... almost erotic.

And then it didn't!

The damn shaving cream was being dashed all over his nose and he couldn't breathe. He shook himself awake, thrusting his hand out to push away the creamed brush, only to find it was no brush at all, but the warm sticky tongue of Annie the Dog. Annie was apparently concerned the Judge was oversleeping and decided to get him on his feet. He supposed that's what you did if you were a dog. You tried to get your puppies on their feet as soon as possible. Unfortunately, Annie had snacked on left-over garlic mashed potatoes the night before. Her breath was awful.

He rousted himself from the bed and ran into the bathroom, stripped off his pajamas, and washed his face with cold water, spitting several times into the sink.

Trying to get away from the scent and the taste of stale dog breath and garlic.   Annie followed him in, apparently satisfied she'd done her duty.   He was up and moving and, in her estimation, no longer sick.   She seemed proud of her handiwork.

Ralphie peeked in at him around the doorframe to see what all the hawking and spiting was about. Ralphie was practicing his spitting himself these days and getting pretty good, using his dad as a model the way sons do, much to the consternation of his mom. The Judge winked at the young man, who tried to wink back.   Ralphie's winks still needed some work.

"You're really big dad," said Ralphie, looking at the Judge's exposed plumbing, then looking down toward the middle of his Lost Boy pajamas where his own pea-shooter was hidden.   "Like Mr. Harry."

"What?" said the Judge, swiveling around in the middle of his shave, suddenly focused, but his young son was gone, likely off to run his truck into more furniture.

It was ten a.m., not that late really, and Katy was sitting in the breakfast room in her white terrycloth robe, have tea and paging through the paper.   He sat down beside her and gave her a tentative smile.   Things had been strained between them since he'd taken Laura's case, but the case was coming to an end.   He truly loved Katy, and he didn't want her irritated with him. It was time they smoothed out their relations.

"I was thinking the same thing, Judge."

"What?"

"What you were thinking just now as you looked at me."

"You can read my mind now, Katy?" he asked, his smile widening.

"Sometimes. You're thinking it's time we put this dispute behind us and move on, me and you. And little Ralphie."

"Yes, Katy, you got me. That's exactly what I was thinking."

"So was I, Judge. So was I."

"How do we start with that, Katy?"

"Tell me about your case, Judge. Bring me back into the fold. Tell me what's going on. Are you going to win this one for the Wilsons? It's almost over isn't it?"

"Yes. All but the closing statements on Monday." He liked talking about his work, as most men do, and she knew it. It was his calling. It defined him. But he'd been tip-toeing around the subject with Katy since their unpleasantness. He'd missed talking out the issues with her, using her as a sounding board, getting her female perspective, invariably different from his own.

"The Strand case is like the old parable about the elephant and the blind men, Katy. The one who touches the trunk proclaims the elephant is like a thick snake. The one who touches the ear says no, the animal's like a giant kind of fan. The third touches a leg, declaring it to be like a tree, and the forth, touching the tusk, says, 'You're all wrong, it's like a spear.'"

"So, the players in your trial are like the blind men?"

The Judge smiled. "Perhaps less honest, Katy. They've mixed their impressions about the case with their own internal devils and professional agendas."

"How so?"

"I think in actual fact the evidence against our clients was so weak that a case should have never been brought in the first place. But District Attorney Nancy Aragon desperately needed a big case to dig her re-election campaign out of the cellar. And old Judge Ferguson was amendable to go along because it suited the needs of his re-election campaign. They both see the case though their political filters.

The press wants to sell newspapers and expand viewing audiences, creating profits and bonuses from an expanding advertising base. They're in a competitive heat to beat each other with the latest news scoop. And they lust to prove they're investigative reporters, breaking out secret news and conspiracies for the protection of society, so they can pat themselves on the back and declare they serve a higher purpose. They see the case more fluidly and have grappled with it in the ways they can to create sensation, notoriety, controversy and public discussion.

Gibson, the therapist who interviewed Ralphie and the other children, has complete confidence in the validity of his methods to get at the truth of what happened to the children. But his methods start with the presumption that something did happen. That's a view contrary to the law, which requires we presume people innocent until proven guilty. He has economic interests in promoting his methods, more fame, more counseling work. Further, I suspect he has his own personal devils to contend with. He refused to answer when I asked if he'd ever been sexually molested as a child.

The children are mostly confused. So much attention, so much counseling, so much time spent practicing answers, so much pressure from parents, the prosecutors, and the community at large, all convinced the Wilsons are guilty. So much to remember. And then the harrowing cross examination. I feel sorry for them."

"And the jury, Judge. What about the jury? How will they see it?"

"I guess that depends on how good a job Barney and I've done in presenting the picture of a different kind of elephant, Katy, an animal we believe more correctly resembles the reality."

"Maybe people in relationships are like your blind men too, Judge."

"How so, Katy?"

"Each partner in a relationship is multi-faceted. And our perception of our partner is imperfect in many ways. We only see some of the facets of our life partner to start. Over time, more facets are revealed through experience and discourse. But I believe we never truly know the full inner workings of our life partner's mind, never see or fully understand all of his or her facets."

"I certainly don't understand the workings of your mind, Katy. That's why living with you is such an adventure."

Annie the Dog shoved her muzzle onto the Judge's thigh craving attention too.

"Yes, Annie. It's an adventure living with you too," said the Judge.

"So, Judge, which facet of me do you like best?"

"That's easy, Katy. You're my sex-pot lover." This earned the Judge a sharp jab in his ribs by Katy's elbow, for which he let out a pitiful yelp. This roused Annie the Dog, who thought the Judge was sick again and reached up to lick. Her garlic scent was still vivid.

"So, what about Jeffrey Simpson, Judge? Are they going to charge the Wilsons with his murder?"

"The D.A. wants to. I'm sure they're working up a case, even though it would by necessity have to be all circumstantial."

"What do you think happened with Simpson, Judge?"

"He was a truly troubled man, Katy. But we know he didn't commit suicide. He was murdered. Someone out there is responsible for his death."

"Do you have suspects?"

"Oh, Katy. Too many. You need to take a ticket. There's Laura Wilson herself, of course. But I can't believe she'd ever do something like that."

"Okay, let's forget Laura, Judge. In fact, let's pretend from now on Laura never existed if you don't mind."

331

"Okay, okay. There's Laura's brother, Harry Wilson. He seems protective of Laura, almost to the point of jealousy. I think he knew Laura and Jeffrey were having a steamy affair in the late afternoons in that tiny maintenance room. Not only did it offend his sensibilities, it jeopardized the very business of The Strand. The pre-school was built on the confidence and trust the parents had in its staff. I think he hated Jeffrey Simpson. If Jeffrey said he was going to blab about his affair with Laura, perhaps because Laura had dumped him and terminated his employment, Harry would have a strong motive to act."

"Did you ask him?"

"Sure. He says he didn't kill Jeffrey. What else would he say?"

"Okay, who else?"

"Well, there's the drug peddler. I call him Narrow-Eyed Jack, but he goes by just Jack. I think Jeffrey was distributing drugs for Jack at The Strand. Jeffrey may have kept sales money he was supposed to send back to Jack. Suddenly, Jeffrey had a huge wad of cash to throw around and burn, and at the same time he trying to stay out of sight. Jack's a tough customer. He'd cut Jeffrey's throat in a heartbeat if he thought Jeffrey was stealing from him.

And Jack has a boss, someone upstream who was buying the drugs and sending them down the pipeline. And there was someone fronting the cash as the capital to make the whole illicit enterprise work. I don't know who these people are yet, but if Jeffrey stole drugs or money from these people, they'd have a powerful incentive to take action."

"That's sounds like a solid play with Jack the Druggie, Judge. I vote for old Jack. But who else is there?"

"Well, Jeffrey's mom, Elaine Simpson, is a piece of work. She didn't much like her younger son. Her older son, Erwin, walks on water. But she had nothing kind to say about Jeffrey, no sympathy for his plight, didn't seem sad he was gone. More interested in the life insurance policy she holds on Jeffrey's life and when that ship might come in. She let slip it was a very large life policy. She seems pretty much broke right now and I suspect badly needs the money. Elaine Simpson's not strong enough to lift Jeffrey up onto those rafters. But with a little help from son Erwin perhaps, or someone else... it could have happened that way."

"I can't see a mother killing her son, Judge. But go on, who else?"

"There's this army buddy of Jeffrey's, Sam Reynolds, got hurt in the dust-up in Afghanistan with Jeffrey. May have been Jeffrey's fault. I don't know. Sam lost his best friend in it. And he suffered permanent injury to one eye.

"Is Sam angry about what happened over there?"

"He doesn't seem to be. Says it was just one of those things. Says it was war; shit happens. Sam befriended Jeffrey after they met up again in L.A. and was one of the few friends that didn't walk away as Jeffrey's life spun out of control."

"Who else was Jeffrey involved with?"

"There's an ex-wife, Louisa. Goes by Louisa McFarlan now, her single name. Dumped Jeffrey after he came back from overseas. Couldn't deal with his PTSD. Hardnosed real estate lady. The kind that takes no prisoners. She had a life insurance policy on Jeffrey's life too. Got it in the property settlement as part of their divorce."

"So, she might be eager to see it cashed in."

"Yes. Again, she'd not be big enough to lift Jeffrey up and hang him from the rafters in the maintenance room alone. But here's the thing: she's got a new boyfriend, Sean Black, a big guy. The pair could have done it. And Black let slip that even before Jeffrey's death, Louisa told him she was going to come in to a $750,000 pot of money and would help him start their own business. I think it was insurance money. How'd Louisa McFarlan know the policy was going to pay off when Jeffrey was still warm and walking?"

"That's very suspicious, Judge. Anyone else?"

"Clair Henderson, Jeffrey's on again off again girlfriend. Seems harmless enough. Subscribes to the philosophy of having two or three lovers at the same time. Sounds like fun to me." This earned the Judge another sharp elbow from Katy.

"Anyway, Clair Henderson says she has this very possessive lover. Very territorial, jealous. He suspected Clair was bedding someone else and got very angry. And he's connected in business with the

Chicago mob. Sounds like a real sweetheart. If he found out about Jeffrey and Clair, he may have decided to eliminate the competition. I haven't talked to the guy yet because Clair is so scared she refused to give me his name."

"Again, sounds promising, Judge."

"And there's two surfing buddies, Katy. I talked to both. They both seemed pretty innocuous, but both had a falling out with Jeffrey. Who knows."

"There's even Oliver Hardy, the Ocean Hill police detective who threatened me in an effort to get me off the case. His daughter went to The Strand. He's convinced she was molested. He's very angry, hot headed, kind of a bully."

"That's not a list, Judge, that's a parade."

"I know."

"You said Jeffrey was dealing drugs from The Strand maintenance room."

"Yes, I think so."

"Could it have been just an angry customer. Or maybe someone who got a bad batch of drugs and got sick? Or perhaps someone bent on stealing his inventory?"

"Possible. I don't know how we'd ever find someone like that, since forensics didn't turn up evidence of anyone else's presence except Laura Wilson's."

"I'll bet I know what they found on the daybed that belonged to Laura Wilson, Judge."

"Katy! We weren't going to talk about her, remember?"

"Sorry. What about the way Jeffrey Simpson was killed, Judge?"

"What do you mean?"

"Well if someone was going to steal his drugs, they'd just hit him over the head, or perhaps knife him or something. And if you were angry about bad drugs, maybe you'd just shoot Jeffrey. But to hang Jeffrey up from the ceiling. Wow, it's almost like a ritual killing."

"By God, you're right, Katy. That's one reason I love you. I think you just came up with the key to this thing."

"You think one of the angry parents decided it was Jeffrey molesting his kid? Decided to take his own justice? Our maybe a couple. If our Ralphie had been molested by Jeffrey and I found out, I might have killed him myself. Motherhood is a strong motivator. I would have made sure he suffered."

"Not quite that. But I think you're very close to the center of the thing, Katy. Let me think about it a bit."

CHAPTER 47

The prosecutor's closing statement focused on the children's testimony and the medical opinions provided by their medical expert, driving home the latter to prove the existence of a crime, and the former to link the crime to the defendants. Armstrong rattled on for two hours, exhausting himself, the jury, and everyone else, finally concluding:

"You might ask why the children kept quiet about what happened to them, ladies and gentlemen of the jury. There are two reasons. For several of the children, knowing no better, they formed emotional bonds with Harry and Laura Wilson, their tormentors. They didn't want to rat on these authority figures in their young lives.

For other children, fear kept them silent. These children were scared out of their wits by threats of bodily harm to them and their parents. Threats backed by bloody demonstrations, the hacking to pieces of small animals and other Satanic rituals.

In closing, I'd like to go back to the fundamentals of the prosecution's case, which we have proven.

Awful things were done to these ten children. Terrible, evil things. Things that should never have occurred in their young lives. Things, the seeds of which they will carry forward forever and which will blossom into pain and emotional issues over their lifetime.

You've heard from these ten children yourselves. You've heard the awful things done to them, and at such a tender and formative stage. You've heard their stories here on the stand and seen their testimony in the private video consultations conducted by Dr. Gibson. They may have forgotten some of the details here and there under the withering cross examination of the two seasoned defense attorneys. Who wouldn't? Wouldn't you?

And these are very small children who have been subjected to the ugliest invasions of their bodies. It's no wonder they've locked away these painful and humiliating memories and now find it difficult to remember some of the details.

But ladies and gentlemen, these ten children... these ten children... they're all saying the *same thing*.

They were repeatedly forced to take off their clothes and perform nude at The Strand Pre-School.

They were repeatedly forced to perform while photographs and videos were taken of their so very young bodies.

They were repeatedly touched on their private areas by the hands, mouths and genitals of adults.

Painful things, hands, fingers, thermometers, and other objects were repeatedly thrust into their most private body cavities.

They all say there were molested at The Strand Pre-School.

And who do they say did this to them? Who?

They all say it was the defendants. They all have testified that Harry Wilson and Laura Wilson did these things to them. These two adults forced these young children to submit and perform for the pleasure and sexual arousal of the Wilsons. And for the pleasure and sexual arousal of other strangers the Wilsons brought in.

And when these abused children considered telling their parents about the awful things being done to them, they were further abused and terrified by displays of sadistic torture and killing of small animals to keep them silent.

You can't brainwash ten children into believing they were molested. It doesn't work like that. You can't 'plant' some fantasy idea into their small minds and have it stick so well that suddenly each of the ten children are each saying the same things happened to them, done by the same people.

The same things, ladies and gentlemen, the same things. These ten children are all saying the same things were done to them by the same adults.

Awful things were done to these young children at The Strand. Evil and cruel and vile things, perpetrated on the youngest members of our community who had no way to protect themselves. You cannot rationally conclude otherwise.

And it was perpetrated by the defendants. By Harry Wilson and Laura Wilson. How can there be any doubt after you've heard the children speak?

You've also heard the supporting testimony of our doctor, our medical expert, Dr. Westwood. Physical abuse to the sexual organs of these young children occurred. The defense has tried to confuse this fact, but they cannot.

Even their own medical expert admits physical evidence of molestation in at least two young victims. And their medical expert cannot rule out similar abuse in the other eight children. He doesn't know. But our expert does. He has provided the photographic proof for you to see. And what about the emotional scars these poor young children bear, mental and emotional damage that will fester and grow as these children mature and understand more clearly the awful things done to them.

And so, ladies and gentlemen, the prosecution has proven its case beyond a reasonable doubt. These children were attacked and molested at The Strand Pre-School, and the defendants are the ones responsible.

I now ask you, ladies and gentlemen of the jury, to do your duty as representatives of our community and find the defendants guilty as charged."

Armstrong marched back to his seat, shoulders rigid, head high, a pastor who'd completed his fire and brimstone harangue, now done, exhausted, confidently leaving his work in God's hands.

CHAPTER 48

The Judge stood up and turned around, surveying first the jury, then the people packed into the courtroom. To his surprise he spotted Katy in the back corner, sitting low down in her seat, trying to look inconspicuous. His eyes paused on her briefly and she winked. Thank God. He knew they'd be okay now, he and Katy

He turned to look at Armstrong and his young pretty colleague, and then up at Ferguson, disapproval etched across the Judge's face. Some people had worried more about election campaigns in this trial than they had worried about faithfully carrying out the sacred duty as lawyers to assure a fair and unbiased trial to determine the truth of the matters at hand.

The Judge slowly walked over to the jury box and rested his arms on the rail along the front row. He looked at each of jurors separately, letting the tension build. Then he smiled at them.

And by God they smiled back. Shit, they smiled back… at least most of them. He was going to do this thing. Damn, he was going to do it.

"Ladies and gentlemen of the jury, you only need to use your common sense here, and exercise it within the confines of 'reasonable doubt', which defines the very essence of our judicial system.

We have a justice system of laws in this country. Not a system of opinions, nor a system of prejudices, nor biases, nor a system by fiat. We don't even have a system based on what we hear in the press from their so called 'credible' sources, despite the widespread assertions made against the defendants in newspapers, radio, TV and the internet.

A defendant is presumed innocent unless the prosecution can prove the defendant guilty 'beyond a reasonable doubt'. If there is any reasonable doubt about the facts and circumstances alleged by the prosecution, then you must find the defendants not guilty. That is our judicial system. It is designed to protect me, and to protect Mr. Armstrong, and to protect Judge Ferguson, and the mostly news media audience in this courtroom. And it is designed to protect each and every one of you, and your partners, and your children and grandchildren." The Judge looked at each juror again as he spoke.

"You've heard the testimony of the children here, inconsistent, half forgotten, easily persuaded that in fact nothing happened at The Strand.

Testimony haltingly given after heavy coaching by Mr. Armstrong and his staff. And testimony given after heavy coaching by each child's parents in a misguided belief they already know the truth better than you the jury, who are the ones charged with finding the truth under our judicial system.

I don't begrudge the emotional involvement of the parents, and their need for revenge for what they believe happened to their children. But they have no right to be the arbitrator of the facts in this case. And no right to endeavor to stack the deck by coaching their children on what they should remember and what they should say.

But I do condemn the therapist, Mr. Gibson, who initiated this whole witch-hunt by creating his own internal scenario of what went on at The Strand.

He infused the children with false memories of things that never happened, through guile, leading questions, sexually explicit dolls cast in mean stereotypes of the defendants, and persistent badgering of the children until he got them to say what he wanted them to say. All to fit his scenario of what happened. He even used gamesmanship, leading his young charges to believe it was a game. A game they had to play. A game in which they had to produce the right answers. His answers. Or be labeled, 'not smart', 'not truthful', 'dumb', not 'cooperative'. A game he would continue to make them play until they spoke his 'right' answers.

Ladies and gentlemen of the jury. You've seen the videos of his interviews. You've seen for yourself what he did to these children. He's planted false memories of events that never existed. Events now believed in these children's minds which will likely haunt them for a long time..

Did he do it for economic gain, the follow-on business of therapy for these kids? Did he do it for the attention he got, national headlines, press interviews, the doting attention of distraught parents who hoped their kids could be 'fixed' in his clinic? Or perhaps to satisfy his own internal demons which he couldn't control. Recall I asked Dr. Gibson if he'd ever been abused or molested as a child. And he refused to answer, ladies and gentlemen. He refused to answer.

At any rate, after all this attention, is it at all surprising that that children's stories more or less track each other as the prosecution points out? Of course the stories 'track'. They've been made up out of the same whole cloth, a cloth manufactured in Mr. Gibson's mind and implanted in our young witnesses here.

As our own Dr. Towns opined, the resulting testimony of the children reflected in the videoed interviews has no probative value. And with that said, their testimony here in court is equally suspect.

Can anyone on this jury say in good conscience, right now, this morning, that they fully believe the testimony of these poor unfortunate children, who have been subjected to this enormous pressure. Pressure to produce Gibson's story of what happened, and then to comply with the coaching requests of their parents and attorney Armstrong.

Can you say to yourself, ladies and gentlemen of the jury, right now, 'Yes, I believe these children's' stories 'beyond a reasonable doubt'? That is, I have no reasonable doubt they are not telling the facts of what happened at The Strand Pre-School?...

I think not.

If we can't accept the children's' testimony as genuine facts of events at the Strand beyond a reasonable doubt, then the prosecution's entire case falls.

There is nothing else to tie any alleged molestation to The Strand or the defendants.

"You've heard testimony from their medical expert that ten of the children were molested. You've heard testimony from our Dr. Flint that only two of the children 'may' have been molested. Whether two or ten, that's awful to hear. And if it occurred the culprits should be punished. But if it occurred, it could have happened anywhere. Playground, doting uncle, playmate, self-exploration, any of a hundred venues. The point is, there is nothing to tie the event, if it happened, to the Strand Pre-School.

Finally, let me go back to my opening statement. The prosecution has presented the defendants as the leaders of a sex ring of molesters, doing unspeakable things to children while taking photographs and videos of their twisted obsessions.

And what did I say then, and what do I say now?

The State has employed three D.A.'s full time, five D.A. investigators, and fourteen investigators. Twenty-two Sheriff's Task Force investigators have investigated six hundred and ninety-five families about The Strand Pre-School and its teaching staff, and four other pre-schools, along with the help of one full-time Ocean Hill Police detective, two full-time FBI agents and seven part-time FBI agents. The State has searched twenty-one residences, seven businesses, thirty-seven cars, three motorcycles and one farm, looking for child pornography, nude pictures, records, diaries, evidence of mutilated animals and bank account records. Their investigation has been carried out at a cost to the state of more than one million dollars.

And what has the state found?

Nada… Nothing… No evidence whatsoever…. There is no photographic evidence, no pictures, no elicit movies of naked children, no traces of blood or semen found in The Strand Pre-School, no hidden passageways, no buried animals, no hidden tunnels beneath the school. Absolutely no corroborating evidence of any sexual abuse or molestation.

Why?... Now we know why. Because the stories are all made up. Fabrications flowing from Mr. Gibson's mind into the children's heads through those unseemly interviews.

In summary, ladies and gentlemen, the prosecution has not carried its burden of proof. There is no conclusive evidence that any child was molested, nor anything to tie the defendants to any alleged crime. There is no way to conclude beyond a reasonable doubt that the defendants have committed any crime here. And under our system of juris prudence which protects us all, and is based upon a presumption of innocence, the defendants must be found 'not guilty'."

The Judge turned and went to his seat beside Laura at the defense table, leaving a silent courtroom to digest his words..

CHAPTER 49

The Judge maneuvered his convertible into a parking space on Highland Avenue in North Ocean Hill, near where he'd parked before, three spots up from the intersection with 40th Street.

He'd driven by the intersection first, confirming Jack, his drug dealing friend with the narrow eyes was at his usual spot again at the corner, sending a poison loaded hand out now and then to supply drugs to passing customers. The Judge got out and walked along the street to the corner, admiring the two women in tight elastic uniforms striding into the corner gym there, looking healthy and fit. He really should start a gym program he supposed, but hell when was there time?

Jack's narrow eyes flew open in surprise as the Judge whipped around the corner, then shifted into murderous looking slits as he surveyed his perimeter, checking there were no police around, calculating what he might do to this out of shape guy twenty-five years his senior.

His left hand slid toward his rear pocket where the shape of a large pocket knife pressed out against the fabric of his distressed jeans.

"You're the guy that put those cops on me, Homes. I know who you are. You're dead meat."

The Judge shoved both hands up in the air, palms out, in front of him, whispering urgently, "I just want to talk."

"It's too late to talk. I owe you big time and I'm paying you back. Almost got you in the bar, and then again on your driveway in Palos Verdes. But old Jack isn't going to miss a third time. Oh, no. My third time's going to be a dream." His mouth twisted into an ugly sneer.

"You got me wrong, Jack. I didn't snitch on you."

"Sure, Homes. You just happened to try a buy on me and then get on your cell phone, and the police just happened to show up two minutes later."

"I saw you at The Strand Pre-School in the early evening the other night, in the furnace room, looking for Jeffrey's stash of drugs."

Jack looked stunned. Surprise spread across his face as he tried to process this connection.

"You were the one in the maintenance room."

"I have what's left of Jeff's stash. Remember, you found it and then had to run off. I thought perhaps you might want it back."

"Listen, pal. Those don't belong to Jeff. Never did. He took them to distribute, but he never paid for them, see. You'd best give them over to me right now, so as you don't get hurt. You got them in your trunk or something?"

"I found two bags of pills. How many did Jeff have?"

"I set him up with a six thousand pills, that's six bags. He was supposed to pay me back weekly, but the fucker never came through with the money. Started ducking me instead."

"I didn't find that many bags."

"Don't shit me. How many you find?"

The Judge stayed quiet, just looking at Jack, showing no fear. He's much like a wolf he thought. If I try to run, he'll take it as weakness and attack, probably stab me in the back.

"Look, pal. Let me explain how it is," said Jack. "This is big business, see. There's a lot of money in it. I'm just a... a cog. I have a boss. I have to account to him. My boss has a much bigger boss, a banker guy, who provides the money to buy the stuff for us and other organizations. You don't ever mess with the big boss. He kills people for a living. Anyway, we all have to account, see.

Either I return the goods, the OxyContin, or the money's accounted for, or... or someone dies. Maybe several people die. Maybe even me. Cause the street on Jeff's advance was fifty a pill, fifty thou a bag. Six bags, that's 300 large. So don't shit around here. How much of my inventory did you find and where is it?"

"You ran off with two bags from The Strand furnace room, Jack."

"Yeah, so? I'm still four bags short.

"Where'd you get it?"

"The OxyContin?"

"Yeah."

"That's none of your concern. You just pony up the pills and maybe you live."

"I heard someone bought OxyContin from Jeff and died. Heard the stuff you gave him wasn't pure. Synthetic junk mixed with poisonous chemicals." The Judge was making it up, but he had to keep Jack talking.

"Hey, man. It's all synthetic. But it's all good shit, right from a doctor's office at the VA. Someone overdoses on it, or mixes it with other stuff, that's not on me. You going to hand it over, or we going to do this the hard way?"

The dealer's eyes flared in anger, and something else. Perhaps the prospect of administering the 'hard way' to the Judge was more exciting than hard.

"Tell you what. I'll sell them back to you at half price. Twenty-five thousand a bag."

"You're a fucking idiot. You want to die right now, Homes? There ain't going to be no fuckin' buy-back. You give me my stuff. Now."

The Judge let his face look worried. It was surprisingly easy to do.

"Okay, okay. The shit's in my trunk. I'm just around the corner. I parked in front of the gym."

"Let's go. How much did you find?"

"Two plastic bags."

"Shit, where's the rest of it?"

They started to walk around the corner toward where the Judge's car was parked.

"That's all I found."

"That mother-fucking Jeffrey. I knew he sold the shit and kept the money. Was having such a good time, spending our money like a sailor. I gave him a warming. Clipped his dog. Figured that'd shake him out of his ways; scare him into turning over the money he owed, but it did no good."

"You kill him?"

"Hah. I just learned about his school gig after he killed himself, selling shit out the basement of a pre-school. Bastard was clever and stupid at the same time. He's dead now. It was an appropriate ending for old Jeffrey. Doesn't matter I didn't get him. Though I'd have enjoyed doing him. Would have made it real slow."

"You sure this stuff not just made up in somebody's garage. Might be impure."

"Naw. I've made pickups for the boss couple of times. Stuff's legit, fresh as a daisy."

"I'll bet I use the same doc. The guy over at the VA in Westwood," said the Judge.

"I doubt that. Our guy's real careful. Wouldn't deal with someone like you. Besides, he don't do retail."

"On the third floor, room three-oh-eight." It was a bluff, but the Judge figured it was worth a try.

The dealer's eyes widened.

"You deal with Doc Stevens?" Jack asked, stopping now and turning to the Judge, giving him a careful second look. "Naw. You're bullshitting me. You just heard the name from Jeff or somebody.

Come on. It's getting late. I want my shit back now, or what's left of it."

"How long you been selling OxyContin on this corner?"

"About a year. I got my regulars. But I sell other stuff too. I sell whatever my customers want."

"You must move a lot of product."

"I do okay. Twenty grand a day moves on my route here on the corner, and I have a couple of other spots my crew covers."

"Is Sam Reynolds one of your crew?"

"Who?"

"Who's your banker?"

"Erwin… What the fuck. That's none of your business."

"Erwin Simpson?" asked the Judge, making another guess.

"Sometimes you can know too much for your own damn good, pal. Just shut up and keep walking. Keep your hands where I can see them."

"So, Jeffrey's own brother is at the top of your ring," said the Judge. "No wonder you couldn't kill Jeffrey."

"I said shut up!" There was a burr in Jack's tone now, a combination of anger and frustration.

They had reached the Judge's car and were moving around to the trunk.

Behind them two motorcycle cops pulled up to park in front of the gym. They got off their bikes and undid their helmets at a leisurely pace, but Jack stiffened, panic spreading across his face. He sensed a trap.

Then Bill O'Neal, the Ocean Hill Police Chief, stepped out of the gym's door, flashing his badge in one hand and his service revolver in the other, pointed at Jack's chest.

"Step away from him, Judge. We've got all we need on your wire. Mr. Drug Dealer here is going away for a long time."

The Judge stood back as the two motorcycle officers sprang into action, leaping forward, turning Jack around, cuffing him, patting him down.

The Judge walked back into the gym, opened his shirt, unhooked the wire apparatus and handed it back to an assistant who'd set up on a folding table just inside. He suddenly felt drained and very shaky. Practicing law was a lot easier than these extracurricular activities.

CHAPTER 50

The Judge was lying in bed considering how to get his aching head from his pillow to the aspirin bottle in the medicine cabinet in the bathroom. It seemed a long way away. The dinner at the Mexican restaurant the night before, with way too many double margaritas, had never boded well for the next morning. How he now regretted his excess.

But it had been a dinner with Barney, and Katy, and Barney's long-time wife, Sandra. Their role in The Strand Case was over now, over at least until a jury decision came in. Then they'd have to see about an appeal.

It had been a long and arduous case. Stressful, filled with long hours, days of drudgery, boring research, moments of self-doubt and even terror as they faced the paper, discovery and motion onslaught of the prosecution.

At the restaurant they shared vignettes and war stories of the case with each other and with their wives, who listened attentively, happy to have their husbands back, proud of their modern-day Don Quixote's who dared to challenge a system bent on burying the accused..

Not surprisingly, the evening had extended long and liquid into the night, until the joint had closed. He had a vague recollection of handing the car keys to Katy and collapsing in the passenger seat, and later being helped to bed.

The phone rang, jangling his headache.

The law clerk on the other end of the call was short and quick, "Jury's in... ten o'clock. Barney will see you there."

The Judge made it to the bathroom and fumbled with the aspirin bottle, then with the two pills, losing one to the tile floor. "Damn!" he muttered, his head exploding in a ball of pain as he bent over to snag the downed pill.

Fifty-five minutes later he tried to walk straight and look alert as he entered the courtroom and slumped into his customary seat next to Laura at the defense table, where she immediately reached for his hand to squeeze and then hold for a moment, sliding her chair closer to his, needing the proximity.

The courtroom was packed, reporters with pencils in mid-air suspension over their notebooks, the two artists at the ready, colored chalk in hand over pads, Armstrong and his pretty assistant in their tight suits and bland ties looking guardedly optimistic. Like sharks waiting for the kill to swim out from under a rock. Barney looked his usual relaxed and rumpled self. The Judge sported his red striped suspenders inside his blue blazer, which he fiddled with nervously.

The jury shuffled in under the stern eye of the Ferguson, who asked the defendants to rise, which they did. A paper was passed by the foreman to the bailiff to Ferguson, who opened it and read it with a poker face. He then looked up and across the assembled courtroom with his usual sour expression, handing the paper to his clerk, who intoned its contents to the suddenly silent room, silent as a church. The final scene in a morality play appearing across the county in a thousand courtrooms in the very same way as society's justice was dispensed.

"On count one we find the defendants not guilty. On count two we find the defendants not guilty. On count three…" and so it went.

Of the fifty-two counts charged, the jury found the defendants not guilty on forty counts charged against both defendants. On twelve counts charged only against Harry Wilson, involving allegations of physical molestation of two specific children, the jury was hopelessly deadlocked and could not render a decision. It was a mistrial on those twelve counts.

The defendants were free to walk out of the courtroom and go back to their lives. Lives deplete of their once thriving pre-school business, deplete of the house Harry had to sell and their respective savings expended to fund legal expenses. Their ordeal was over. But their victory was a hallow one.

The courtroom broke into pandemonium, Ferguson pounding his gavel with no effect. Laura jumping up and hugging the Judge while Harry Wilson jumped Barney, pounding him on the back with relief. The two prosecutors slumped in their chairs, the consequences of defeat spreading across their stunned faces.

There was a mighty logjam at the back of the courtroom as the reporters tried to exit at the same time, desperately trying to reach cell phone space where they could report the verdict, a nasty loss for the Los Angeles County District Attorney Nancy Aragon.

As Laura headed toward the small gate at the front of courtroom, a wildly silly smile on her face, the Judge in tow behind, the Judge heard Armstrong hiss at her under his breath from the prosecution table, "This isn't over, Ms. Wilson. We'll refile on the twelve counts on Harry, and we're going to put you away for the murder of Jeffrey Simpson!"

CHAPTER 51

As the Judge parked his car, he could hear from a block and a half away the pounding of the surf on the beach. Another tropical storm in Baja had brought titan surf to L.A.'s beaches. It wasn't cold really. And the sky was a bright blue between white puffy clouds. But the air hung with moisture. It felt like Hawaii. He took his yellow waterproof nylon jacket from his trunk and put it on.

As he strolled across The Strand bike path and cut across the sand toward the concrete ribbon running into the sea that was the Ocean Hill Pier, he could hear the full roar of the surf, taste its salt in the wind, feel its dampness in the soft sand under his feet. He looked out to the end of the pier.

The huge ugly structure, all heavily concreted, supported on large concrete pillars, slashed out into the middle of the roaring surf and just beyond, like some giant indestructible monument from another age, perhaps a hastily cobbled together landing pier on Normandy Beach. It gave no quarter to the pounding surf, which churned as from a giant cauldron around its end and along its sides, engulfing the concrete ribbon in spray and mist, soaking everything and everybody who might venture out along its surface.

As the Judge watched, a powerful chunk of rolling green water sluiced up against its seaward pilings almost to the rail on the pier's end, before tearing under the pier to smash against its underside and concrete supports, throwing a heavy wall of water and foam landward. The Judge had never seen waves so high here. The entire pier should have been shuddering under the onslaught, like some snake caught in a trap. But the pier stood firm, rigid against the sea, creating even more explosive power at its tip as the waves tried with brute force to dislodge it from its shoring's.

He stopped, considering his options, wondering how wet he would get out there. A lone man in a blue breaker stood at the pier's end, his back to the lee wall of the little rotunda there, sheltered from the surf and wind. Sam Reynolds.

The Judge supposed if Reynolds could go out there so could he. He turned his collar up over his neck and struck out, bending low into the force of the wind, walking quickly, trying to make the end of the pier and the sheltering wall of the octagon between two very large waves. Trying to avoid the puddled water on the pier's planks. Trying to stay dry.

The Pier surface had water puddled everywhere. He could feel his shoes salty and wet, his socks soaked. He wished he'd worn boots. Angry foam rose up on either side of the structure, licking at the railings like some angry dragon.

The Judge finally reached the relative shelter of the little octagon structure at the pier's end. He pressed his back against the lee wall of the octagon for support, next to Reynolds.

"It's a fucking great day!" yelled Reynolds. Yelling was the only way to be heard over the roar of the surf. "I love the wind and high waves. It makes me feel alive."

"It's a hell of a place to meet, Sam," the Judge yelled back. "I'm soaked, wind-blown, and damn near deaf."

Reynolds shrugged.

"Why'd you come Judge? You figured it out, didn't you? I can see it in your eyes. You're one smart asshole."

"About Jeffrey?... Yes. But I needed to be sure."

"There's no certainty in life, Judge. Only chaos. I'm afraid you've misplayed your hand."

"When I laid it all out, Sam, who had motive? Who had access? Who knew about Jeffrey's little distribution center in The Strand basement? Who had no alibi? Who had the brawn to lift Jeffrey up and hang him on that beam? Who had medical training, a corps man you said, and now a hospice nurse. Likely access to the Succinylcholine used on Simpson?

And most of all, there was the ceremonial nature of the kill, Sam. Jeffrey was hung like a common criminal."

"Which is what he deserved."

"Yes, well, you also let it slip when we first talked that you were sorry Jeffrey had been killed. But how could you know he'd been killed, murdered? That it hadn't been a suicide? The autopsy hadn't been completed yet. It was all there. It became obvious in the end."

"I knew when you called. Asking for one more meeting. There was a tinge to your voice. Something. I knew."

"Was it because of Jimmy and Tony? Your buddies in Afghanistan who died because Jeffrey made a mistake?"

"Right on, Judge. Jimmy and Penn. Jeffrey was a stupid, hopeless screwup. A drunk and a druggie who couldn't keep his head on straight. All he had to do was follow Sarge's orders. But he was blitzed to the gills with meth. Couldn't see straight. Drove our truck right into the landmine like it was deliberate. Drove Jimmy and Tony and Penn into eternity. Then know what? Know what he did as he got us blasted all to hell, Jimmy gutted like a fish on the seat next to me, Tony screaming for his mother, Penn all blown to pieces?"

The Judge shook his head.

"Jeffie laughed. He just laughed at all the blood, at all the pain, at Sarge screaming he was an idiot. He laughed at me with my face cut up, and poor Jimmy beside me, his intestines spread over my lap, his head resting on my shoulder, puking the last of his blood down my shirt. The asshole just laughed. He thought it was funny. Jeffie deserved to die. It had to be done. For my buddies, for their families. He was a useless piece of shit and he deserved a miserable death."

"And so you gave it to him?"

"Yes." Reynolds smiled, remembering, a wild look in his eyes now. Jeffie wiggled like a fish at the end of that rope while I held his hands together. I waited until the drug wore off some before I eased the stool out from under him. I didn't want to break his neck. Too quick. I wanted to see him swing, kick with his feet, do a little dance of agony for me. And that's

361

what he did. It felt good to see the terror and anguish in his eyes, watch the light there slowly fade, then go out. I wanted him to see it was me. To understand it was payback. To know why he was dying."

"And then you watched it again, didn't you, Sam. Over and over. You recorded a video of the whole thing on a DVD, and you watched Jeffrey dying over and over again."

"You know about that? You are a clever bastard, Judge. Yeah. I've got the DVD in my glove compartment; shows it all. Shows me putting the belt around his neck, the fear in his eyes, me easing the stool out from under him while he's slowly kicking and trying to scream, coming down from the Succinylcholine, trying to get his words together, trying to plead, 'don't do it', pissing his pants. It felt so good, so right."

"You've no remorse, Sam? Jeffrey was weak. But he was a fellow human being. You were mates once."

"Jeffie wasn't human. He was an ugly scar that needed to be peeled away so I could breathe again, go on with my life."

"Did you consider the consequences of killing him, Sam? Even with a PTSD defense they're going to put you away for a long time. Either in prison or in a hospital."

"No. No, Judge. I couldn't stand that. I'm only just now free. Only now feeling alive again. Now I've done what needed to be done. No one's going to lock me up."

Reynolds backed away three steps along the octagon's wall, then pulled his hand out of his pocket.

There was a revolver in it, aimed at the Judge's chest, a Smith and Wesson J-frame .38.

"You're not going to tell anyone, Judge. No one's ever going to know."

"You're going to shoot me, Sam? You'll never get away with that." The Judge's skin had suddenly turned sweaty under his jacket.

"I'll shoot you if I have to Judge. But I'm proposing to give you a fair chance, sort of." A wild smile spread across Sam's face. "You know how to swim?"

The Judge nodded, eyes on the gun. Another damn big black hole in the universe pointed at his chest.

"You're going to jump, Judge. You're going to jump into the sea right there."

Reynolds nodded at a break in the pier railing, and a ramp going down halfway to the water for access to utilities under the pier, blocked by a handrail locked in place, but still assessable.

"You're going to jump, or I'm going to shoot you in the stomach right now, drag you over there, and push you over. How do you want to go into the sea, Judge? With or without holes?" Sam laughed. "It's your choice."

The Judge looked at the gun, held steady, a finger curling around the trigger, tightening. Then he looked at Reynolds, his eyes flat now, cold, no hint of emotion. He wished he'd not been so cavalier, coming out here alone. It had been a mistake. Reynold's was right, he'd misplayed his hand.

"And if I survive, Reynolds? If I make it to shore?"

"See that's the best part, Judge. You won't. Once you're in the water, I'm going to toss this gun and dive in after you, yelling, *Man Over Board. I'll get him.*'"

"You're crazy."

"Like a fox. See, anyone who sees us will think I went in after you to save you. But remember I went through Ranger training. We trained in surf just like this. So I'm coming after you to make sure you drown."

Reynolds' eyes were somewhere else now.. He was seeing it all in his mind's eye. Relishing the rush it would bring. He was totally unhinged.

"Turn around now, Judge. Move it. To the rail. Let's go."

The Judge slowly turned around. Reynolds viciously shoved the gun into the Judge's back, making him gasp with pain, forcing him to the rail and to climb up over it and down on to the ramp.

"Okay, Judge. You want to play? You going to jump? Or shall I just shoot you here?"

The Judge looked down at the churning water, green with white foam in the shadow of the pier, swirling around the pilings. It was a lousy choice. He took a big breath… and jumped…

CHAPTER 52

The Judge landed feet first, sinking immediately beneath the waves, his air almost knocked out by the force of the fall and the strength of the water. Tons of water piled on top and around him, throwing him this way and that. He kicked up his shoes and struggled to pull his jacket up over his head and off, leaving it zipped.

He kicked to the surface, tied a knot in the arms of his jacket, and thrust his arms up, holding the bottom of his jacket open, puffing it with a little air, then desperately tied its bottom off too. Hoping for some buoyancy from the trapped air.

Another wave came down on top of him then, sending him deep under a wall of water that felt like concrete. He hung on desperately to the jacket and kicked back up to the surface, then twisted and did his best to swim away, away from Reynolds, away from his gun, away from the pilings being bashed by the surf. But it was hard. There was an undercurrent pulling him back toward the pier, trying to suck him into the pilings, trying to make him a human pinball.

He went under again, an even bigger wave piling on top. He swam under the water then, still trying to get away from the pier. When he could hold his breath no longer he came up, fortunately between two rollers, treading water, gasping for breath, lungs on fire.

He turned and looked back, saw Reynolds jump into the water after him, swimming out toward him with long, measured, powerful strokes. Rolling his body with confidence over the top of the first wave to hit him. Sam was a powerful swimmer with broad shoulders and long muscular arms, and he cut through the water like a shark. There was a demonic look on his face, powered by an intensity of force and purpose that wouldn't be stopped. The Judge was exhausted from fighting the undertow trying to drag him under the pier. He was in trouble.

But then a rogue wave appeared from nowhere, not ready to crash, lifting the Judge high in the air, toppling a foot past him, crashing down with immense power behind him, presenting itself at an angle to the pier, bigger than anything that had come before.

It crashed down on Reynolds as though he were a toy duck, sweeping him with lightning speed under the pier, into the pilings, smashing his head into the first piling, then spinning him around into more pilings, bouncing him like a ping-pong ball from one piling to another, smashing his head, his shoulders, his back. The wave washed the underside of the pier with its might as it continued its headlong rush for the shore, leaving Sam's body behind. But Sam lay limp now in the back wash, head down in the water, unconscious, or dead. Then another wave picked Sam up and started the brutality all over again.

"That could be me," thought the Judge... "Joss."

The next huge swell arrived, lifting the Judge up as he struggled against the undertow still trying to carry him under the pier, so tired now, close to giving up, hanging on for dear life to his improvised yellow coat float. The top of the swell gave him a view of the distant beach, and midway out two orange buoys streaming in his direction, pulled by yellow lines attached to two bobbing heads, dark crewcut hair, powerful strokes cutting the water, bringing the heads ever closer.

Lifeguards!

Using his last reserves of strength, he struggled some more against the tide, spitting out salty water, ignoring his stinging eyes, near collapse.

Suddenly there was an arm around him. An orange buoy was thrust under his arm and then another under his other arm. The lifeguards sped off with powerful strokes, swimming north and slightly out to sea, towing him away from the pier, out of the riptide. Eventually they turned landward again, where a third lifeguard materializing from nowhere, joined them, helping to tow him in toward the sand.

Some nasty rollers lifted them up and shoved them down. Twice the Judge was smashed into the sand, but he held on with a death grip to the orange floats. Finally he was half walked, half dragged by two exhausted lifeguards up the sand, allowed to collapse at the top, a few feet from the grasping fingers of the hungry waves.

He just lay there, panting, coughing, slowly noticing the siren of an approaching paramedic truck.

Thank God. He didn't suppose they'd have a gin and tonic aboard. But it'd be okay. He'd accept whatever they had.

He knew intuitively Reynolds didn't make it. Perhaps there was some natural justice in the world, something beyond the man-made variety he'd spent his career trying to support.

CHAPTER 53

The Judge explained to the squad car police what happened while they checked him out on a stretcher, looking for a concussion and anything else beyond the cuts and bruises from multiple collisions with the bottom on the way in. They said he was lucky. Perhaps he was. But he just felt tired.

At the Judge's urging the Ocean Hill Police searched and found Reynolds' car, an old Chevy, parked up on Ocean Drive above the pier. They opened the car, searched the glove compartment as the Judge suggested, and found the DVD. It was all there just as Reynolds said, a complete video of the murder of Jeffrey Simpson at the hands of his old army buddy. Case closed. Laura and Harry Wilson dropped as suspects. At least there was that.

But the Judge felt hollow somehow. How had he miscalculated so badly, putting himself in such serious jeopardy? And what had gone wrong at the VA, leaving Sam Reynolds to twist in the wind, never receiving the help he should have got as a veteran? Left living on the edges of society, festering over a perceived injustice he felt compelled to right. And how had the country failed Jeffrey Simpson as well, a veteran driven into a place of despair, forced to deal drugs just to get by?

The human animal was a creature with the ability to hold on to and to feed all sorts of complexes, anxieties, guilts, and associations, once wrong-wired at conception, at birth, by experience, or by all three.

The creature had begun as an adaptive animal on the plains of Africa, blessed with a pair of opposable thumbs, damned with a coil of hidden emotions wrapped in a small head, and stuck with a penchant for violence. Nothing had changed much in the intervening centuries.

CHAPTER 54

The Judge and Katy settled on the sofa at home, Katy laying against the Judge's shoulder, her legs across the brocade material to rest on the sofa arm. It was dusk. They watched the lights come on aboard two tankers in the Santa Monica Bay, off El Segundo at the end of The Strand. The firefly lights of airliners in the LAX pattern appeared in the deepening violet sky, framed by the darker Santa Monica Mountains and the curve of the coastline around to Malibu.

"So, what's it all mean Judge? You've told me the sights and sounds of it, but what's it really mean? Jeffrey Simpson selling drugs out of The Strand, his own brother the head of his drug ring, his VA doctor suppling the opioids. And I have visions of his murder at The Strand, hung like a side of meat from the rafters of the maintenance room.

And the Strand Pre-School. Allegations of child abuse. Ralphie being videotaped, the panicky press blitz, the community outrage, the endless TV coverage, The Strand Police Chief refusing to charge, those poor little kids trying to tell what they could remember, or had been programmed to remember, pounded into the ground by you two bullying defense attorneys.

Now Laura Wilson's been found not guilty, and it's a hung jury on whether Harry Wilson was molesting those little kids. Was there child abuse, Judge? Did the system fail those little kids?"

"The system isn't a guarantee of justice, Katy. It's a set of rules, process, and presumptions, better than anything that's gone before, but not perfect."

"So, sometimes people get away with it."

"Yes. I'm afraid so. Our system pre-supposes people are innocent until 'proven' guilty. And it sets a very rigorous procedure for the 'proving' part. Built around common people from the community asked to listen to all the evidence with an open mind, listen to both sides' interpretation of what happen, and then find as a unanimous group whether in their judgment the defendant is guilty beyond a reasonable doubt."

"But the press said they were guilty."

"The press says lots of things, sometimes with an aim to raise emotions, heighten drama, and encourage audiences to buy papers and watch news shows. Ratings and circulation can mean everything in their business."

"But the press said they had credible sources for the information they blasted out."

"Hah! The press doesn't have much of a definition for what constitutes a 'credible source'. In the scientific community, there are rules for what we consider to be credible information, more often termed 'verifiable', peer reviewed, reproducible experiments and the like. There are at least some objective standards. But not so much in the world of journalism."

"What constitutes a 'credible source' if you're a journalist, Judge?"

"It's whatever the reporter thinks is credible, and whatever the publisher is willing to publish or the producer is willing to allow on his show. Sure, some newspapers are more 'credible' in their reporting than others, but that just highlights the inconsistencies in how the word is used. Credible is whatever the newsman think it should be, and is sometimes shaded by the organization's agenda, be it political, economic or social."

"So, the New York Times, the Wall Street Journal, NBC News, when they run a story based on 'credible sources', that's more reliable than when the National Enquirer, the National Examiner, or the Globe make a similar claim in one of their stories."

"It is, Katy, although they all have their agendas. But I think that misses the point."

"How so?"

"In the courtroom, there are rules for determining what is credible testimony; the Rules of Evidence. They're designed to get at the facts and to protect core values of our justice system. That the accused is innocent until proven guilty. That he has the right to confront his accusers. That the decision on guilt is made by his peers."

"So, Judge, when the press runs a story based on their credible sources, you're saying the community is inclined to judge the accused without those protections?"

"That's it. Society becomes a mob, steered this way and that by the press. People are fired, reputations are ruined, political campaigns are lost, deals don't get done, families are destroyed, memberships are canceled, relationships terminated, some people never get work again in their chosen field; all consequences of someone's 'credible source'.

"So, were children molested at The Strand, Judge? You still haven't answered my question."

"Katy, the answer is… I don't know. But under our system of Justice, neither Laura nor Harry are guilty. They've the right, just like you and me, to be presumed innocent."

CHAPTER 55

The Judge relaxed at the circular dining table in the crowded meeting room at the Beverly Wilshire Hotel, gently playing with the rubber chicken with his fork. The Los Angeles County Bar program had just concluded and now everyone could eat. The California State Bar required all attorneys licensed in the state to complete continuing education classes every three years in order to maintain a law license. Something of a joke really, since the courses involved a large time commitment but were rarely relevant to anybody's particular area of practice.

The Judge's table was full, ten attorneys looking as blurry eyed as he did after listening for an hour and a half to a long-winded explanation of terminable trusts. They mostly dug with gusto into the chicken, apparently determined to get their money's worth. The Judge waited for dessert, turning back to the conversation he'd been having with Ben Folsom, a young lawyer across the table, the son of an old colleague.

The Judge had literally watched Ben grow up, some three years out of law school now, married with a young daughter, and settled as an associate in a large Los Angeles law firm.

The topic of discussion had been how District Attorney Nancy Aragon had just lost her election bid to keep her office. Naturally, this turned to a discussion of The Strand Pre-School Case. The Judge couldn't restrain himself. Like a large fish broaching the surface for a fly, he launched into criticism of a system that allowed defendants to be tried in the press before there was ever a legal trial to determine the facts.

Ben Folsom immediately sat straighter in his chair, eyes suddenly blazing, pointing a knobby finger at the Judge's chest, shaking his head with anger.

"You're wrong, Judge. You're absolutely dead wrong!"

"What?" The Judge was startled. He was just warming up to his topic. And he wasn't used to being told he was dead wrong by a junior lawyer with limited experience.

The Judge looked at Ben across the table, Ben's face was red and contorted with emotion now... even anguish.

"My daughter went to The Strand Pre-School, Judge. She never, never had an infection before. But over six months at The Strand, Mary suffered three separate urinary infections... If we'd only been more careful...!"

XXXXXX

The Strand

NOTES FROM DAVIS MacDONALD

I hope you enjoyed reading "THE STRAND" as much as I enjoyed writing it, and perhaps here and there it made you smile a little.... Please leave a REVIEW for me on Amazon if it was a positive read.

Recent events once again raise the specter of a society which demands the Public's 'Right to Know' be placed ahead of the constitutional principles which declare a person innocent until proven guilty, utilizing the rules of due process under our law. Recent events also demonstrate again the willingness of media to sensationalize and editorialize beyond their function to report the verifiable facts of the news, and a willingness of society at large to accept such embroidered news at face value and to judge, condemn, and ostracize members of the community based on these sensationalized accounts in the press. Accounts which may or may not be born out as fact in a court of law.

We remain as a human community subject to the all too human tendency to be swayed by words, emotions, prejudices, and excitable gossip. But when our community's judgements are made based upon reports in the press. And when the journalist's 'credible source', named or unnamed, is accepted at face value as the truth. We find ourselves destroying reputations, careers, and relationships of individuals without due process.

In these instances, we, the community, become little more than a mob.

This novel is entirely fictional, as to plot, places, characters, events and in all aspects, but it is inspired in part by several high-profile cases involving alleged child molestation, including the famous McMartin Pre-School case which stemmed from allegations made against the owner and teachers of a pre-school in Manhattan Beach, California. At the time in the 1980s it was the longest and most expensive trial in U.S. history. From the point when the first charges were filed against the defendants, it took seven years and two trials at a cost of over fifteen million dollars, to be resolved.

The two primary defendants, the owner operator of the school, and her son, were denied bail, and languished in jail through the first trial. The school was closed, several fires were set there at various times, and ultimately the business and property were lost by the defendants, along with other assets, used to finance the legal costs of their defense.

The seven defense attorneys concluded the evidence against the defendants was weak and elected to mount a defense at the preliminary hearing which lasted eighteen months alone, with witnesses called and cross-examined, including thirteen children who it was alleged had been molested. The defense effort to have the charges thrown out was unsuccessful at the preliminary hearing stage, and the court ruled one hundred and thirty-five charges were to be carried forward to trial.

An intervening election resulted in a newly elected District Attorney, who reviewed the case and ordered charges dropped against four teachers at the school and the mother of the owner operator, leaving only two defendants who proceeded to trial, the owner operator, and her son.

The widespread publicity accompanying the trials was rife with supposed facts from asserted creditable sources that later turned out to be without basis, or what we'd call today false news It made it difficult to gather an unbiased jury, and difficult for the defense to line up qualified experts willing to testify on behalf of the defense.

The first trial lasted almost three years, and resulted in a finding of not guilty on one hundred and twenty-two of the charges against the owner operator and her son, and a hung jury unable to conclude guilt or innocence on thirteen charges leveled solely against the son.

A second follow-on trial of the son on eleven of the surviving charges again resulted in hung jury. At that point the District Attorney gave up further prosecution.

You can read a fascinating account of this case, well documented, written by people involved in the defense, in the book, *Anatomy of the McMartin Child Molestation Case,* by Edgar W. Butler, Hiroshi Fukurai, Jo-Ellan Dimitrius and Richard Krooth, University

Press of America, Inc. copyright 2001. ISBN 0-7618-1983-5.

ACKNOWLEDGEMENTS

A grateful thanks to those good friends who helped me to write and edit THE STRAND. Dr. Alexandra Davis, who was the first to see every word; my amazing Editor, Jason Myers, who did yeoman work on the edits and kept me on the straight and narrow; Justine Prado, the screenwriter so helpful with the plot for this novel, the multiple good friends that agreed to read and comment on the early draft, and Dane Low, (www.ebooklaunch.com), who helped me design the distinctive cover Also of special note, Mark Goulston, M.D, whose insights I borrowed for the difference between depression and the more serious questions that may suggest suicide, and Harry Plotkin, my old classmate from USC Law, from whom I borrowed his clever insights on jury voir dir.

THE STRAND is a Work of Fiction

The Strand is a work of fiction. Names, characters, businesses, cities, organizations, clubs, places, events and incidents depicted in this book are either products

About Davis MacDonald

Davis MacDonald grew up in Southern California and writes of places about which he has intimate knowledge. Davis uses the mystery novel genre to write stories of mystery, suspense, love, and commitment, entwined with relevant social issues and moral dilemmas facing 21st Century America. A member of the National Association of Independent Writers and Editors (NATWE), his career has spanned Law Professor, Bar Association Chair, Investment Banker, and Lawyer. Many of the colorful characters in his novels are drawn in part from his personal experiences and relationships (although they are all officially fictional characters).

HOW TO CONNECT WITH
Davis MacDonald

Email: Don@securities-attys.com
Website: http://davismacdonald-author.com/
Twitter: https://twitter.com/Davis_MacDonald
Facebook: Davis MacDonald, Author
Blog: http://davis-macdonald.tumblr.com/
LinkedIn: Davis MacDonald

**Amazon Author's Page:
Davis Macdonald-Author**

THE LAKE...

The Judge will be back in late 2019 with Book 7 in the Judge Series, THE LAKE. What follows are the first two chapters of

THE LAKE
A Mystery Novel
Set in
Southern California

CHAPTER 1

The Judge couldn't sleep. He quietly shifted the covers off, trying not to wake his bride Katy, twenty years his junior. He stuck one bare foot and then the other off the high bed and onto the cold wood floor. From there he raised his considerable bulk to sitting and then slid off the bed and tiptoed across the floor, out into the hall, and down the rickety stairs to the mountain cabin's main floor. He passed the old grandfather clock at the foot of the stairs which had belonged to his great great grandmother. It read 1:33 a.m. He let his breath out in the living room, apparently successful in his attempt to not wake Katy.

The cabin was old. Even older than the Judge. 1908. It stood testimony to the early pioneer spirit that settled Lake Arrowhead at the beginning of last century, a simple two-story cottage, built low on the lot, hanging over the Lake and its private dock. Wood-burning fireplace, potbelly stove, no insulation, plywood interiors aged in golden brown from all the years.

The Judge's family had modernized it here and there over the century and the generations, forced air heat, new kitchen, basement built out into a game room and a bedroom, attic now a combination bedroom and office. The footprint hadn't changed, but the space had grown to some twenty-five hundred square feet.

The Judge had inherited the cabin, *Whispering Point* was its name, when his mother died, and although he didn't get up to Lake Arrowhead often with his busy schedule, it was still a sanctuary for him. Clean air, the crystal-clear Lake reflecting sparkling blue skies, and nights filled with a thousand stars. The cabin was set on a semi-peninsula jutting out into the Lake. At night the lapping of water on the Lakeshore whispered up through the pines to the cabin's open windows, hence the cabin's name.

He looked out the open living room windows now, almost floor to ceiling, opened outward, bringing the night in. There was a large yellow moon, shooting a broken yellow ribbon across the rippled Lake surface, victim of a slight breeze from the northeast. He could hear, and almost taste, the soft lapping of the Lake's edges against the shore, sending a calliope of sound floating up around the cabin. It was so very peaceful. Like a church.

A boat started up somewhere across the Lake, a fast speedboat with a big engine and noisy pipes, droning like a distant bee in the background, making the surrounding silence even more precious. Someone was up late. Perhaps coming home on the water after a pub-crawl in the Arrowhead Lake Village.

The Judge took deep breaths, sucking in scents of the Lake, the trees, and the intermittent brush, feeling his soul replenished in some measure by the air and the pure quiet romance of the place.

But there was a gradual disquiet from somewhere. What was it? The boat across the Lake with its buzz-saw engines was drawing closer, invading the pristine silence like a noisy thief. He wished the guy would get to his dock and shut off his damn engine.

The buzz grew closer, and noisier, and closer and noisier, until it felt like the damn boat was under his feet, like the cabin floor was pulsating in step with the boat's noisy pipes.

Then, suddenly, there were ripping, tearing, screeching sounds. The sounds of fiberglass and aluminum ripping through a wooden dock below his feet. His dock. The night was torn by bright orange flames leaping skyward beneath him, the thunder of the explosion engulfing the cabin, serenity destroyed. The blast knocked the Judge back on his heel as his hands went up instinctively to protect his eyes from the stabbing light and the blast of hot charged air buffeting through the open window.

Shit. Someone just crashed into his dock.

CHAPTER 2

The Judge stabbed his bare feet into his nearby shoes and pounded down the stairs, out through the game room to the deck, and down the ancient stone stairs toward his dock, his progress illuminated by dwindling flames on the water.

There was a boat there, or what had once been a boat, more like two thirds of a boat now, upside down on the water, its smooth bottom immodestly exposed for the world to see. Bits and pieces of what had been the whole were nearby in a puddle of burning fuel floating on top of the water, the small flickering flames licking experimentally at the remains.

The Judge dashed down the wooden steps that led onto his dock, or what was left of his dock. The outer half of the dock no longer there, defined only by a jagged boundary of broken wood and shredded float where it had once been.

That's when he saw what he feared. A lone body floating face down beside the overturned hull, half submerged, not moving. He jumped into the water beside the dock and waded out almost to his neck, splashing away puddles of burning fuel in his path. With a long reach he collared the back of a Tommy Bahama shirt and stumbled his way over the rocky bottom back to the little beach, dragging the body up onto the coarse sand and turning the man over, sinking into the sand and pulling the head on to his lap.

The eyes were rolled up into the top of the man's head. There was a deep searing gash down one side of his skull, blood and bits of dislodged grey matter oozing out.

But the Judge recognized him all the same. It was a friend, a fellow attorney, a neighbor from across the Lake in Shelter Cove. It was Jerry Stone. Jerry was very dead.

The Judge heard faintly, and then louder, the sound of sirens on the highway further around the Lake. A Lake patrol boat roused from the Dam Marina was also setting out, a spotlight sweeping an arc from its bow across the surface of the Lake as it aimed in his direction. Lights were going on in cabins up and down the Lake on either side of him, concerned residents nosing out to see what had happened.

So much for the serene evening on The Lake.

Katy emerged on the edge of the terrace above him, Annie the Dog at her side. She peered over the edge, her hair tousled, a robe thrown around her.

"Are you okay, Judge. What happened? You didn't fall in the Lake again, did you?"

The Judge sighed. One small slip off the dock two years ago and he'd been forever marked by his wife and dog as prone to falling in the water. Someone who needed to be carefully watched. And scolded periodically lest he forget his brush with a watery death.

The Judge looked down at the face of his friend in his lap. Jerry hadn't missed that appointment.

He gently laid Jerry's head back down on the sand, stood up, brushed sand from his soaked Nautica PJs, and began a slow ascent up the sixty steps which ran up the side of the lot to the street above. He waved his hand in the air to attract the attention of firefighters scrambling off their truck, arms filled with equipment and spotlights, trying to assess how to get down to the water. The glow of their truck's strobe light alternatively washed the surrounding pine trees in reds, lending an unreal and macabre atmosphere to the scene.

Finally, the fire team came tearing down the steps, meeting the Judge half way, then tearing past at his direction. Later a team member came down with a collapsible stretcher, and in due course all three came back up, hauling the stretcher, unfolded and flat now, occupied, a clean sheet tucked over poor Jerry's body. The night had just gotten interminably longer.

The sheriff's department showed up in the form of two officers, one younger, late twenties, a redhead with a pink face and freckles under his bright blue eyes. The other was older, senior, sporting a large paunch that made it more difficult to clamber down the stairs to the dock, evidence of too many years, too much stress, too many donuts. The Judge gave a statement while a second boat showed up from the Dam Marina, lights flashing back and forth across the Lake in front of his cabin, the two boats setting up booms to corral the floating fuel.

This was a resort community that made its living off the surrounding opulent second homes of the rich, and the hordes of weekend and day-trippers enticed up the mountain in the winter and summer from the Great Los Angeles Plain. The Lake had to stay pristine at all costs.

After he finished his statement, the Judge thought he was done, but a Lake Patrol Boat pulled over to the floating back half of his dock and a young woman jumped off. She bounded up the stairs to the top of the bluff below his cabin, waving for him to come down. Dressed in tan uniform and peaked cap with the Arrowhead Lake Association emblazed on it, she cut a pretty figure, tall and buff, slim legs, high breasts, and flat stomach. As she got closer, he saw black curls tucked under her hat, pale white skin, heavy eyebrows, and dark brown eyes that held a twinkle, even at this ungodly hour in the morning. The slant to her eyes suggested Middle Eastern or perhaps Turkish roots somewhere up her tree.

"You're the Judge," she called as she got closer, an engaging smile lighting her face. "Least that's what everyone calls you."

"I am," said the Judge, smiling back despite the aching weariness descending upon him like a heavy blanket.

"Is that 'cause you're a Judge?"

"Use to be. Been retired by the voters for some years now, but the nickname still sticks."

"Well, Judge, you need to take better care of your dock."

"Yes. Half of it seems to be missing."

"Seriously, without the front floats under it, the balance of the dock is likely to sink into the Lake if the wind comes up. Best call your dock contractor this morning. We don't want it going into the Lake, do we?" He got the big smile again, softening her words.

She was face to face to him now. She smelt faintly of florals, fresh fruit, and mildew, perhaps of combination of Daisy Eau and dock lines. Her eyes looked openly into his, filled with interest and concern. He had a feeling they might have met in a former life, been something more than... friends.

She perhaps felt it too. She blushed and looked down for a few seconds.

"Okay, Judge. I'm Ally Monroe. Commander of the Lake Patrol." She stuck out a small hand, slender fingers and clear nail polish, the hands of a concert pianist. He shook her hand, noting the feel of the calluses here and there from working rough lines and driving boats. There was a slight electric shock to her touch, a mini-current, not unpleasant, in fact arousing. And then it was gone. She was gone. Bounding back down the steps to her waiting boat.

The Judge finally climbed back into bed about four a.m., thoroughly chilled, though he'd changed out of his soaked pajamas somewhere along the way. He moved his icicle feet over against Katy's warm thigh, seeking solace, only to be met with a yelp, and a firm hand pushing him back to his side of the cold bed. The frontier value of sharing discomfort and grief was lost on Katy.

But Annie the Dog jumped up on the bed and settled her fur against the top of his feet over the blankets, lending much-needed warmth. He drifted off, visions of a goddess dressed in tan, arising from the flames of a watery hell, tinting his dreams.

Xxxxxxx

Look for THE LAKE, available in the Fall of 2019

DO YOU ENJOY A GOOD MYSTERY NOVEL?

Don't miss **"THE JUDGE SERIES"** available on Amazon (search 'Davis MacDonald'), on kindle, in paperback, on audiobook, and in fine book stores.

THE HILL: Book 1: A retired Judge puzzles out the reasons for a teenager's death in one of America's richest communities, uncovering greed, corruption, illicit sex and murder. What started as a favor for the girl's mother becomes a duel with powerful forces, threatening the Judge's reputation, his freedom, and finally his life. In this same crucible the Judge finds new purpose, burning through a sad and solitary existence, reaching out to forge an extraordinary relationship with a younger woman. A woman put at risk by the forces that wish to end the Judge's quest for the truth.

THE ISLAND: Book 2: Catalina Island... and Avalon, a sunny village just off the Southern California coast. It seemed the perfect place for R&R over Memorial Day weekend with the new young woman in the Judge's life. But what he stepped into was gang violence, civil disobedience, bitter rivalries, infidelity, and even murder, ripping the social fabric of the small town asunder.

From Avalon's Yacht Club, through its alleys, sidewalk cafes and swank watering holes, across its private beaches and beyond, to the Airport in the Sky and the party cruise ship sitting offshore, the Judge tracks a shadowy killer. And as the town is forced to fight for its very existence against overwhelming odds, the Judge finds his romantic relationship compromised by an old flame, forcing him to examine and re-define his own past before he can risk a new future.

SILICON BEACH: Book 3: Attacked on Santa Monica Beach, the Judge knew he'd made more than his fair share of enemies over his ten years on the bench. But this came out of the blue... or did it? So starts the Judge's desperate search along the boardwalks of Venice, through the tony bars and restaurants of Santa Monica, the yuppie ghetto of Playa Vista, and the clubs of West L.A. as he relentlessly pursues adversaries who threaten him -- and anyone who gets too close to the secrets buried in Silicon Beach.

All the while the Judge must try to negotiate compromises required to maintain his new marriage to a woman twenty years his junior and come to terms with the child she carries. As the Judge closes in on his adversaries and the body count mounts, he fears his new bride and the child may become collateral damage in this deadly contest with conspirators who risk all to win all.

THE BAY: Book 4: It was to be a minivacation on Newport Beach's golden sands for the retired Judge and his young wife, now very pregnant. But it turned that morning into something else. He'd agreed to do the FBI a small favor. But now there was a murder. He found himself head to head with one of America's most subversive societies. Evidence implied a plot, but to do what? Wreak havoc on Orange County's foremost amusement park as the FBI suspected? Or something more sinister?

As the Judge sets out to identify the murderer, his FBI partners suddenly turn antagonists, determined to stop his investigation at any cost. Who to believe? Who to trust? How to balance claims of National Security against the right of the victim and his family for justice and closure? And all the while trying to cope with his young pregnant wife, unstable and depressed, not the person he'd married, testosterone coursing through her system as her body prepared for the birth of an unplanned son.

CABO: Book 5: Cabo San Lucas looked to be a great get-away. Until bodies started falling off roofs. The Judge finds himself caught amongst shifting loyalties as police and politicians scramble to hide corruption reaching to the highest levels of Cabo society. Murder in the boardroom, assassination of reporters, an attack on the beach, Katy kidnapped, the Judge frustrated at every turn as he tries to solve twin murders, save his new bride, and escape the wrath of a network dealing in modern-day slavery and human misery. Follow the Judge through the labyrinth of raucous watering holes, exotic restaurants, pristine beaches and tawdry red-light districts, as he stalks killers too powerful to stop in the upside-down World of…. CABO.

THE STRAND: Book 6: When the Judge dropped off his young son at The Strand Pre-School that morning he didn't expect to find a body swinging from the rafters of the pre-school's maintenance room. Nor to be dragged into the middle of allegations of sexual abuse of the young charges attending the pre-school. He certainly had no premonition of the immense wave of public opinion about to rise into a towering swell and come crashing down over him, over his bride Katy, and even over little Ralphie, his five-year-old son. Churning them in a cauldron of confusion, social stigma, hate and violence. Upending friends and circumstances taken for granted, nearly bankrupting his law practice, and challenging the very bedrock of his marriage. When his former lover is caught up in a national frenzy as the press and the networks rush to judgment, condemning her for child molestation and Devil worship, the Judge feels compelled to step forward to help his old flame, leading her defense in a cut-throat jury trial, and exposing the real story behind the suicide in the maintenance room of THE STRAND.

(Inspired in part by the facts and circumstances of real cases. all characters, events and story portrayed are fictional.)

THE LAKE: Book 7: The Judge investigates the death of his friend and fellow lawyer in Lake Arrowhead, in the process unearthing scandal, puncturing reputations, outing the deceitful, and stripping away the layer of anonymity from a community infested with secrets. (to be published in late 2019).

Watch for announcements for future books on my Website:
http://davismacdonald-author.com/
Davis MacDonald

WEBSITE

www.DavisMacDonald-Author.com

The Strand